SLIM WHILE YOU SLEEP

The revolutionary, simple and inexpensive way to lose weight, using the amazing mind power of self-hypnosis

VALERIE AUSTIN

BLAKE

Published by Blake Publishing Ltd,
98–100 Great North Road, London N2 0NL, England

First published in Great Britain in 1995

ISBN 1 85782 110 6

British Library Cataloguing-in-Publication Data:
A catalogue record for this book is available from
the British Library.

Typeset by Dacorum Type & Print, Hemel Hempstead

Printed in England by Clays Ltd, St Ives plc

1 3 5 7 9 10 8 6 4 2

INSTRUCTIONS AND DIRECTIONS FOR THE HYPNO SLEEP TAPE

The radical new slimming therapy which you will discover in the pages of this book has never before been published anywhere in the world. It could revolutionise your life, especially if you are one of those people who have an on-going weight problem.

However, if you are to complete the *Slim While You Sleep* programme successfully, you MUST read this section first before doing anything else. It gives clear instructions as to what is on the tape, which you purchased with this book, and how to go about using it in order to achieve your goal.

There are certain things that need to be said to you while you are sleeping, to allow your inner mind to be able to accept the specially prepared suggestions, without disturbing your sleep. It is also an added advantage to give a suggestion, (which is called a post-hypnotic suggestion) while you are aware (in hypnosis) to encourage your inner mind to respond to such words. The solution is to have a two-sided audio cassette tape.

SIDE ONE You will hear my voice guiding you into hypnosis with a conventional hypnosis suggestion, which will encourage weight control and includes the post-hypnotic suggestion. Side one can be used at any time during the day or evening. It does not necessarily have to be used just before you go to bed, or before side two. At the end of the tape you can either open your eyes or enjoy the peaceful relaxation until you are ready to resume your activities.

SIDE TWO You will hear a few words from me at the start of the tape saying, 'and now to sleep, and now to sleep, and now to sleep', these words allow you to adjust the volume; this is followed by thirty minutes of total silence. If you are still awake for a few minutes, do not think that the tape has ended or the tape is faulty, the silence is deliberate, it is intended that during this time you will fall asleep. Later on in the tape, my voice will resume with approximately 6 minutes of suggestions. By this time you will be asleep and the suggestion will enter your most inner mind.

If you are still awake then you may find an alternative method to ensure your tape is playing when you are indeed asleep. You can either ask someone you trust to begin the tape when you are asleep, or use a timer. A timer can be bought, inexpensively, from most electrical shops and will ensure your cassette recorder will begin at the time designated. Side two must only be used as you retire for bed. If you have insomnia or a sleeping problem, the suggestions on the sleep tape will still be of value, but will not have the same impact as they would if you were asleep.

ACKNOWLEDGEMENTS

Without my agent, Roy Stockdill, I would not have this wonderful opportunity to offer this new concept in therapy.

Peter for all his guidance.

Philip and Marion for a dozen lives. For a dozen more.

Gil Boyne, who was responsible for me being involved in this fascinating world of hypnosis.

Kay Keirnan, of the Blue Stone Clinic, whose advice and treatment for my back was invaluable.

Pierre – a fine friend, a talented photographer and wonderful writer; also to Cathy – thanks for the marvellous make-up job.

Malaysia Airlines for the best flights I have ever experienced. Your pilots land beautifully. You take a lot of beating.

To the many new friends I met in Malaysia, and especially Langkawi, an island paradise with all the five-star comforts – the island where I found myself.

Maureen Brockwell, a friend at all times.

Valued friends, Pat and Vic Leslie.

Marisa Peers, a very fine hypnotherapist and innovator.

Philips, one of the companies that helped me when I most needed it; when my computer broke down, immediate help was at hand.

I have spent all my available money on courses to educate myself in mind techniques and when I saw this slogan on a lorry, just as my first book had been published, I realised it had all been worth while:
'If you think education is expensive, try ignorance.'
So a big thank-you to all my teachers.

And last, but certainly not least, to all my students, many of whom I consider as personal friends.

Contents

For Jack Mason – a giver
in this life, not a taker.

*He let me use his life research
without expecting to be reimbursed.
Thank you, Jack!*

FOREWORD

Have you ever heard anyone remark: 'I would be able to lose weight if only I had the willpower'? This is a problem that many face when attempting to lose weight. In *Slim While You Sleep* Valerie Austin offers a solution to this problem, through self-hypnosis. This is a rather interesting way of changing your attitude towards your eating habits and amount of exercise you do, but an attitude change is just what is needed in many cases. Without the ability to put the required changes in diet and exercise into practice then weight loss is never going to happen.

What you eat every day of the year is important and an attitude change will alter this. This is in contrast to many slimming diets, which are seen as short-term deprivation and so, even if initially successful, may not result in a sustained weight loss.

The importance of not crash dieting cannot be over-stressed; the best way to lose weight is through changes in diet and exercise, not by simply starving yourself. If you cut down too drastically on what you eat you will lose weight, but not all of this will be the body fat that you want to lose; some will be muscle and some water. This will mean that when you then recommence your normal eating pattern (which will probably soon follow, as starving yourself is most definitely not an enjoyable experience!) then your body will have a lower energy requirement and so you will need even less food! It is just as important not to overdo any exercise, as your body is likely to suffer through injury.

The most important thing to look at in your diet is the fat content: hidden fats as well as the obvious things like butter, cream and fried foods. Examples of these include full-cream milk, pastry, cheese, biscuits and chocolates. If you are extremely strict with your fat intake, then you will be able to eat more high-carbohydrate, low-fat foods such as bread, rice, potatoes, pasta and breakfast cereals. These are not fattening foods, as some may believe, but they fuel the muscles with carbohydrate. Carbohydrate is used as a fuel supply by the muscles even during the lightest exercise. Without this carbohydrate in the muscles any type of exercise may feel difficult and so less exercise is likely to be performed. If less exercise is performed, less fat will be lost. The fat content of the diet will also determine whether body fat is lost because if you are eating large amounts of fat this will be converted and stored as fat in your body, as will large amounts of alcohol.

Drinking plenty of non-alcoholic fluids such as water, fruit juice and low-calorie drinks is important, as even slight dehydration can make you feel less energetic and so impair your ability to exercise. Taking small, frequent amounts of fluid throughout the day is a good idea. If you wait until you feel thirsty then your body is already becoming quite dehydrated.

Self-hypnosis offers the key to success in putting the sensible diet and exercise partnership into action.

Lisa Piearce BSc, SRD
Sports Nutritionist

INTRODUCTION

FOOD FOR THOUGHT

'It's easy to lose weight – you just eat less, so why all the fuss?'

How many times have you heard this said? When you have a weight problem, this remark is an insult to your intelligence and can be very aggravating. It's easy enough for those who *don't* have a weight problem to utter it in a condescending fashion. But, though the above statement may technically be true, that does not necessarily make it possible to achieve it – for, if it were that easy and simple to get thin just by eating less you would always be slim. End of story. The nightmare of trying to stick to something as simple as a diet can cause unimaginable frustration and leave a person vulnerable to illness, both mental and physical.

A deep-rooted mental trauma is often the route to being overweight. But with regular use and repetition of the exciting new techniques you will discover in this book –

and with determination and willpower – you can over-ride those harmful old programs that are cluttering up your mind and cancel them out. With the added incentive of extra therapeutic work being made to operate *while you sleep* – which new findings have proved to be fact rather than fiction – it now all depends on YOU.

This book aims to guide you to help yourself to be able to eat naturally without conflict. That is all you require to eliminate your weight problem for ever. When the conflict is gone, self-discipline is natural and automatic. You 'eat to live', instead of 'live to eat'. It is that simple. But to get to this stage it is necessary to keep free for yourself just a few waking minutes a day – and the rest of the work is done while you sleep. Is that asking too much?

A method that is so simple and quick it seems impossible that it would work . . .

First, a few facts about the dieting business. Dieting is a multi-billion-pound industry. Virtually every day, new fads and fancies flood the market, luring diet 'addicts' into spending yet more cash on trying out the latest slimming craze and so-called 'wonder' weight-loss programme. Yet what is the truth? For the great majority of would-be slimmers, *diets don't work!* They find themselves trapped in the never-ending spiral of dieting, losing weight for a while, relapsing, piling on the pounds again, trying yet another 'miracle' diet, losing more weight, then putting it on again . . . and so on . . . it's a depressing vicious circle, often seriously detrimental to their health, to say nothing of mental frustration.

Diets based on food deprivation, or only eating certain

types of foods, vary from the silly to the downright dangerous, but they all have one thing in common: they relate to a purely *physical* approach to slimming and ignore the *mental* element. However, there is growing evidence that being overweight is a *state of mind*. Lack of willpower is widely acknowledged as the principal reason why so many slimmers 'fall off the wagon'.

What is needed is an approach to weight loss that combines sensible eating with a disciplined program of mental self-help and self-control. In a powerful, two-word phrase, the key to successfully losing weight – and, more importantly, maintaining the loss – is *MIND POWER!* Once you reprogram your mind to root out bad, negative habits and replace them with dynamic new, positive ones, then you should be able to eliminate your weight problem for ever. Think of the mind as a highly sophisticated computer – it's a question of getting rid of the outdated software and inputting a new program to change attitudes.

How to achieve this? Everyone has at their command the most powerful and natural tool for self-healing known to mankind: *HYPNOSIS*. Using hypnosis, those bad habits and lack of self-discipline that lead to over-eating can be eliminated and replaced by positive mental attitudes, resulting in a more balanced approach to a sensible diet and permanent control of your weight problem.

In this book I will show you how you can learn to hypnotise yourself, either alone or with the aid of a partner or friend – and, even more amazingly, how that knowledge can be made to carry on with its beneficial work *even while you are asleep*. I will teach you in easy, simple-to-follow stages the art of self-hypnosis, how to write your own suggestion scripts to guide yourself into hypnosis, how to make and use your own cassette tapes and the unique method for programming yourself to lose weight while you sleep.

The method requires a commitment of only a few minutes every day in order to result in a much healthier lifestyle. You should find that by following the instructions and guidance you will eat in a more positive and natural way, eating only when hungry rather than for comfort or protection.

Included in the book are a variety of already prepared suggestions that cover a wide range of eating disorders to use in your suggestion hypnosis work. The main Hypno-Sleep therapy was pioneered by the discoverer of this exciting new concept, American hypnotherapist Jack Mason, from whom I learnt the technique. The version which I have developed is on Side 2 of the tape which is included with this book.

This book has been designed to give you options. Options to use advanced mind techniques, working with yourself, for yourself – taking responsibility for your actions and your life.

You may be asking, what exactly is sleep hypnosis? Sleep hypnosis enables you, the subject, to direct the inner mind to do the necessary work even before your subconscious is active. To use an analogy, suppose you consult a hypnotherapist to seek help with a problem . . . the advanced hypnotherapist has been likened to a computer expert who shows you how to work your computer and run the software. There are instances that the computer expert would find very time-consuming to deal with; for instance, a malfunction in the design would cause problems. However, if he was in a position to contact the designer and present the set of circumstances or effects, identifying the problem, then the designer would generally know immediately what to do. So, his advice and input may only have taken a matter of minutes, saving hours of searching the computer expert may otherwise have had to undertake.

Sleep hypnosis is like being directly in touch with the designer to correct the malfunctions and solve the problems at source. Your specially devised hypnotic suggestion is rather like the computer expert explaining to the designer what problems result because of the design fault. The designer then makes an adjustment to ensure the smooth running of the equipment.

To give an example of this analogy, you would devise a script to point out the problems and ask for them to be dealt with. If dealing with a specific weight problem, a suggestion may read like this: 'Mary is eating for comfort and she is eating foods that are only destructive to her system. Mary is ready for change and from now on she eats only the food that is healthy and good for her system. She finds she enjoys the new eating habits as much as she ever did when she ate unhealthy foods.'

If the person with the problem was fortunate enough to be able to tell it directly to the designer, thereby bypassing the middle-man (computer expert, conscious or subconscious), then the process of healing would take only minutes to adjust the software program. The computer expert would be superfluous, as would be the subconscious. The laborious job of bringing the traumas to the forefront and dealing with them is eliminated – a quick, clean cure.

This method is very sophisticated but very new and so it needs practice and commitment. Unfortunately, there are no free lunches in this life . . . well not yet, anyway!

1

CHANGE YOUR LIFE
WHILE YOU SLEEP

A therapy more powerful than you could dream!

'Diets don't work unless you don't have a weight problem.'
It's all very well making a statement like this but rarely is it
explained. However, supposing that you were given actual,
factual, explanations of why diets don't work, plus
instructions on how to get over the obvious obstacles that
prevent them working? Add a sort of user manual for the
person who wants to lose excess weight, then you should
have a far better chance of success. You need to find out
what is preventing you from losing weight by the standard
methods and then be able to do something constructive
about it.

This extra knowledge will increase your chances of
achievement a thousand-fold. The new research is only just
beginning to break through and has had scant attention

from the national press. But it is the key to allowing you to be able to make changes in attitude. Changes in attitude are directly responsible for changes in unwanted behaviour, such as over-eating. This information is invaluable to the person who desires to lose that excess weight but can't seem to manage it.

As a result of these exciting new discoveries, techniques that previously were only used by a skilled, advanced therapist in one-to-one hypnosis have now been adapted to the point where we can virtually eliminate the need for a guide (which is the role of the therapist), allowing you to do therapy work on yourself. As in any do-it-yourself method, which is what this really is, a certain amount of commitment from you is essential.

The luxury of going to a therapist is being able to hand over the responsibility to someone else. But the difficult part can be finding a good therapist, one you can trust, which is essential to your belief structure when using hypnosis. There are many good therapists about. However, you may have read quite a lot in the press recently about something called 'false memory syndrome'. This is an alleged phenomenon in which the therapist is accused of planting in the subject's mind information – supposedly being recalled from the subconscious memory in hypnotic regression – which was never there in the first place. The whole area is clouded with controversy but it has put a question mark against hypnosis and brought scepticism into such treatment, which is a shame, both for the client who has genuine belief and the good therapist.

Although rare, the fear of the client when undergoing

hypnosis that information can be induced by the therapist has caused substantial damage to the hypnotherapy business. Therefore, I have written this book as an alternative to give you a chance to work on yourself before a decision is needed to seek expert help. You have nothing to lose – except your excess weight – and everything to gain. Your new options are absolutely safe, with the likelihood of a high percentage success rate to enthuse you.

One thing, though. If you decide to enlist the aid of another party to act as your guide to assist you into hypnosis, which is one method I shall be suggesting, then you must be sure to choose someone whom you trust completely. One way to give yourself more confidence is to tape record the sessions while you are undergoing therapy.

Until now, it has been generally accepted that if a person who is trying to diet has had a trauma early in life which is directly responsible for them being overweight, then that person will be unable to lose weight until this has been dealt with. It is complicated still more by the fact that the trauma may be so deeply buried in the subconscious that the person may not even be aware of it.

The new research I am including in this book I can personally vouch for – it has been one hundred per cent successful for me. It enabled me to get over my father's death without rehashing all the traumas I knew were directly involved, since the same traumas were the cause of a serious memory loss, a memory loss that I had for six years out of ten. The therapy work I had done to retrieve my memory then was very alarming and I was loath to have to go through the same, or similar, tactics to get rid of the anger and frustration I was feeling after my father died.

Even though I was suffering and knew I needed to have some treatment, I took the six months I needed to find this new therapy technique I had heard about in the USA. When it worked for me, I knew there was a very exciting method on the market, more powerful than I could have dreamed of, and I was sure it could be adapted in some way for self-help.

With the advice and help of Jack Mason, who was the pioneer in this field, I carefully designed and adapted the idea, specifically for the person who wants to lose weight but who, like me, didn't want to have to relive possibly unpleasant memories to do so. Not, I must add, that any unpleasant memories that I have unearthed in either myself, or in the thousands of clients I have had in hypnotic regression, have ever caused any regrets about the therapy. In fact, they had the opposite effect. But there are many who refuse to have therapy because of this unjustified fear.

Knowledge gained from the use of new technology is what we have to help us in our goal to keep to a weight we are happy with. Until this year I would have recommended the need to see an advanced hypnotherapist as the only way out for the person who has a trauma-related weight problem. Now there is a new method, though it is not fool-proof, nor one hundred per cent guaranteed. No treatment ever is. In fact, the likelihood of success depends on your own commitment – so, really, it's up to you. We live in a society that seems to take away all individual responsibility for fixing ourselves, so this is it: your chance to take back the responsibility for your own development.

In my travels and learning I have been mainly concerned with hypnosis and how to use the power of the mind to make desired changes. I found that there was a very deep level of healing that was triggered by being guided into a very deep trance, far deeper than is used in conventional advanced hypnosis, far deeper even than needed for a coma state (this is a term used in hypnosis when a person is catatonic) or natural anaesthesia. I first witnessed this phenomenon in the USA three years ago and I decided I would take a trip to America in 1994 to learn the technique for myself. The rest of the year I have spent in putting together a method that is workable for the ordinary person.

The new technique is simple and effective and can be used while you are sleeping. It also generates an excellent success rate. The technique requires the least amount of effort for a change of attitude and behaviour, so that any sensible diet you try afterwards has a chance of working. You don't have to test it; you will know when it has been successful because you will simply be able to cut down eating and you will begin to care what you feed your body. The method is explained in detail in Chapter 3.

Although the best diet of all is common sense, a specially formulated one has been supplied for this book. It combines the most advanced knowledge with easy and inexpensive recommendations from an established Harley Street dietary clinic. It is carefully arranged with recipes to suit the business person, as well as the person with time on his or her hands. These are found in Chapter 5, with hints for what's new on the market that I have personally seen work. There are also exercises to generate quick results, permitting you to work at your own pace. But before you use my technique you need to know a little about the problems that prevent the more conventional methods of weight loss from working.

Here are some of the many questions I get from clients desperate to lose weight:

'I eat less and don't lose weight . . . Why?'

'I am so overweight and, yet, I don't eat much . . . Why?'

'I only have to look at a cake and I put weight on . . . Why?'

'I lose weight and I am OK for a while, then I just go and binge . . . Why?'

'I am constantly on one diet or another . . . Why?

'I'm not too much overweight but I can't seem to lose for long . . . Why?'

'I am a very strong person but I can't control my eating . . . Why?'

'I comfort eat, I just want to eat normally . . . Why can't I?'

So many overweight people just go on from one diet to the next, sometimes losing and sometimes not, but always gaining weight in the end. And ignorance guarantees a captive audience for whatever new slimming idea or gadget appears on the market, securing yet more profits for the billion-dollar business that diets and weight loss command.

I have helped many clients for weight problems with

conventional hypnotherapy, using regression, which helps the client to understand the trauma that caused the unpleasant side effects of over-eating. A popular theory of the moment seems to be that the most common cause of obesity in later life is sexual abuse in childhood but I have to say that I have rarely found this, even with the most obese of my clients. In fact, I was shocked when a report in the press stated that a huge number of fat people were overweight because of such abuse when they were young. I considered how terribly unfair it was for this sexual abuse label to be attached as a generalisation to the overweight. Out of 2,000 clients with *all* types of problems, not just being overweight, I found only a handful of them to have sexual abuse as the cause and they already knew of this when they came to see me for therapy.

When a client first visits me at my clinic for a weight problem, I visually note how much overweight they are carrying and ask how long they have had the problem. It helps to indicate whether it is trauma-related or not, although only in a very general way. Of course, it's not infallible. I still go by the rule: 'Believe nothing you read and only half of what you see.'

If the client is only slightly overweight, say up to 10 lb, and has had the excess weight for only a few years, this can generally be dealt with easily and would probably have a good success rate with suggestion hypnosis, which is simply explained later in this book (Chapter 3). Usually, even relatively slim people have to use a modicum of discipline so as not to over-eat. This is quite normal. It is the failure to control the eating that usually spells out a trauma-related problem – although this can be misleading in itself. For example, if a client suddenly increases their weight by more than 10 lb and has not previously had any problems with their eating, it is hard to make a guess whether this is due to a trauma problem or not. Neither the client nor the therapist can know this for sure.

I had a client who had this type of weight problem. She explained to me that she knew precisely when the problem had started. It was six months previously when her husband had left her. She had never before had a weight problem. It was the amount of weight that really gave it away and the suddenness of the change in behaviour. When she was regressed through hypnosis, it took her back to when she was a little girl of about five years old and her parents were having a very frightening argument, which resulted in her father walking out of the home for good. During the fight she was very distraught and sneaked into the larder where she ate a whole, sizeable cake. The cake did not taste especially good, as she was too upset, but it did take her mind off the disturbing nature of her parents' argument.

When a similar set of circumstances happened much later in her life – the fact of her husband walking out – a question was sent to her subconscious as to what should she do in these traumatic circumstances for comfort. The urge to eat was the response. Every time she felt the pain of hurt she would eat and, of course, after her husband left, this was constant – and so was her eating.

This is a simple example of a trauma-related problem. When she was asked why she thought she over-ate, she assumed it was because of her husband's departure, when really it was only the beginning of an already built-in programme. The *real* source was when she was only five years old.

Someone else may put on weight because they were having problems with their spouse but it may be, in fact, a new trauma rather than an unresolved problem in the past. The information is at hand and it is easy to change the behaviour with just simple suggestion hypnosis.

A more complicated trauma-related eating problem was quite extraordinary. One of my colleagues had a client who weighed 18 stone and had been overweight for many years during her first marriage. She was the victim of a husband who was a wife beater. He would punch her and she even had her teeth knocked out. She was very afraid of upsetting him. The least thing gave him the excuse to be violent and she found she could not even talk to him for fear of reprisals. Instead of talking she would eat, so her words were expressed by eating, two or three helpings at a time, food being the substitute for conversation.

Although her second husband was not at all violent, she still found it difficult to make conversation and still had the bad habit of substituting food for words. When this information was gleaned through regression hypnosis, she was able to change this unwanted behaviour and instead eat only when hungry – and also talk openly. She began to regain her confidence with a character-building therapy and then was able to shed her excess weight.

New reports have shown that it is now possible to tackle this problem with self-help and change the behaviour while in a deep sleep by instructing the deeper level of the mind to do the work necessary – something that has not before been thought possible. I would not have believed it if I had not seen the extraordinary work being done and tried it out for myself.

It is not magic and it takes commitment and perseverance but the rewards can be staggering and life-changing. I, personally, was in a terrible state and full of anger after my father's death and can only be thankful for this new Hypno Sleep which pulled me through. I now find it hard to believe I was angry at all. I cannot logically understand why. This proves the treatment works, when your conscious mind is satisfied.

Why so many diets don't work

Diets only work for the person who doesn't have a weight problem. So where does that leave the millions of frustrated people who do? The multi-billion-pound industry built on food indulgence simply changes the packaging and introduces the same ingredients in a new way. Then all they need do is sit back and wait, knowing that the same people who have bought from them in the past will be eagerly waiting to buy yet another new wonder product that promises to fulfil their dreams to be slim and trim. The same people who have failed miserably time after time, diet after diet, try and hope once again. Maybe this will be *it* at last – the diet that works for them.

Fool the body and the mind will also be conned! Did you know that in the USA there are clinics that treat people who need to *gain* weight. The method they use is to begin by putting them on a diet. Then they take them off the diet and then put them back on it again. This unbalances the system and soon they eat less and yet put more excess weight on – does that sound familiar to you?

This system fools the body. If you drastically cut down your food intake, your system cannot tell the difference between controlled food reduction and famine. Therefore, it acts as if there is a famine, adjusting the system to accommodate. This, in turn, slows down the metabolism and when you start to eat properly again it will store the extra food as fat, adjusting for the lack of food and preparing for a possible long-term shortage of food. This gives an explanation as to why people who go on constant diets do not need to eat in great quantities to gain back their lost weight very quickly – precisely the opposite to what the slimmer anticipates.

So what are the options, safe methods or dangerous ones? Jaw clamping, stomach staples and slimming pills are on the danger list, while an attitude change fits easily into the safety category.

As the Americans say, 'Keep it simple, stupid.' The remarkable attitude change by self-help programming is very simple to follow but does need some commitment. Like learning to ride a bike, anyone can do it but you have to persevere – it doesn't happen by itself.

A few minutes a day practised for twenty-one days can drastically change your life. By the end of it you will be eating in a positive and natural way – eating only when you are hungry instead of for comfort, protection or punishment. Why not take the easy way out and use your mind by reprogramming it, introducing the correct instructions while in a mild trance so you can eat to live, rather than live to eat?

Questions and answers, the facts about hypnosis

There is a lot of ignorance about hypnosis, which unfortunately gives rise to myths and fears. Why should this be, when hypnosis is a perfectly natural tool which is available to everybody? Hypnosis is a state of altered consciousness that happens to everyone, often without you realising it. Everyone daydreams. That is a form of hypnosis. Just before you go to sleep, you are in this daydreamy state. In hypnotherapy you are guided into this state and the state is prolonged by suggestion. *You are not asleep!* The fact is, you are either awake or asleep – one or the other. When you are in hypnosis you are awake, therefore you are aware of everything. If you are awake, you have to be. If you are asleep you cannot be in hypnosis.

Hypnosis can be used to treat a wide range of problems which include: stopping smoking, weight, anxiety, learning difficulties, public speaking, stress, panic attacks, fear of flying and all phobic fears, emotional problems, pain reduction, compulsion, obsessive behaviour and bedwetting. These are just a small selection of treatable mind problems.

It is not just a formula to help you with your problems, it is also a positive therapy that can help you improve your whole life. For instance, if you want to adjust your personality, to be more confident, more positive, happier, better in business, improve at your favourite sport or learn to speed read in one hour, then hypnosis can be a beneficial force in all those cases. It allows you to improve instantaneously without the usual repetition or practice that is normally necessary to learn any habit.

So, what is hypnosis exactly, then?

Hypnosis is a state of mind that we all experience. It has been equated with the moment we wake in the morning or just before we drift into sleep. We exit the hypnotic state to allow us to enter sleep but the transition is so subtle we are unaware when it happens. If you have experienced a daydream – and who hasn't? – then you have been in a form of hypnosis.

So I am not asleep, then!

No! Absolutely not! Not ever! Under no circumstances! But you may look fast asleep to the onlooker and that is where the confusion lies. It is very frustrating for the hypnotherapist, however many years they have served this magical world full of imaginative power, that some subjects still believe they should be asleep.

I remember once being in my rooms in Harley Street. This was a particularly glamorous room and looked like a film set in Beverly Hills, very opulent. I had the chairman of the board of a very large corporate company, a real tycoon captain of industry, in hypnosis. He was so deeply relaxed he was slumped in the chair. When he came out of this especially deep trance, he remarked, 'I wasn't in hypnosis, I wasn't asleep.' Looking back, I regret I didn't have available the video equipment I possess today to demonstrate how wrong he was! I always spend the first half hour in a session on explaining hypnosis and how you aren't asleep. But it doesn't stop this very common reaction, which can be very frustrating for the hypnotherapist.

Can anyone be hypnotised?

Considering all hypnosis is self-hypnosis and everyone has daydreams, which are a light form of hypnosis, the answer has to be 'Yes.' The exception to the rule is the person with brain damage or a total breakdown in concentration. Although I believe that this type of person is far from not being able to be hypnotised but, rather, they are constantly in a natural trance-like state – a permanent daydream, if you like. I have never failed in my practice to hypnotise someone who wanted to be hypnotised.

Certainly, some people are capable of being hypnotised more easily than others. It is generally believed that people who are good at visualisation usually make better subjects. You can test how visual you are by closing your eyes and imagining an object, say a chair. See what colour your chair is, then look to see what it is made of. Open your eyes and ask yourself if you actually 'saw' the chair in your mind's eye or you just knew what it looked like. There is a difference!

If you 'saw' it, then you are a visual person. Sigmund Freud, from his extensive study on hypnosis, estimated that two-thirds of us are visual and the other third are not. I am one of those who are not. We are the type of people who, until recently, hypnotherapists believed were hard to hypnotise or, even worse, not hypnotisable at all. Some highly qualified professionals, even top psychiatrists who use hypnosis, believe this even now.

The late Milton Erickson, a key figure in hypnosis, based many books on different suggestions for people like me. Because I had this problem of visualising, I devised a method so that the non-visual person could be put into hypnosis using the same suggestions as the visual one. I did this by establishing to which category they belonged in the first place, then asking the subject to visualise how they normally did it. So if I say, 'Picture in your mind a garden,' you can mentally swap the word 'picture' for 'imagine', or say 'Imagine you can picture a garden.'

When I did my research, I found that the two-thirds formula seemed to be generally correct. The exception to the rule was when I was working in Malaysia and found that 99% of the clients I saw were visual and only 1% not. This leads me to question the whole subject of visualising. If it is a case of 'What you don't use, you lose,' for example, then not using visualisation after you are a child could lose you the facility. If you are brought up with wonderful, imaginative stories, as in many of the Eastern religions, you are more likely to keep this wonderful tool of visualisation through your adulthood.

Anyone engaged in the artistic world is usually very visual, whereas people dealing with numbers, like accountants, tend not to be. These non-visual subjects are sometimes wrongly categorised as an analytical type of person and dealt with incorrectly by the hypnotherapist. The rapport between the hypnotherapist and client is then weakened.

Can I be hypnotised against my will?

No! If you don't want to be hypnotised, you won't be. You can stop the procedure by refusing to accept the hypnotic instructions and by forcing other thoughts into your mind. Although this can be difficult with a very good professional hypnotist, it is certainly possible. It is comparable to letting a door-to-door salesman into your home and trying not to buy from him. His whole professionalism is based on talking you round. He does it day in and day out. He is going to know all your get-outs and has found ways to use them to his advantage.

Will I be aware of what's happening?

Yes! Most people feel surprised that they don't feel any different while they are in hypnosis, just very relaxed. You actually have more feeling after the fact. When you come out of hypnosis, you realise how relaxed you have been. To use a simple analogy, just because you don't feel the blood flowing in your veins, it doesn't mean it has stopped circulating around your body. When you are in hypnosis you are still aware of what is happening around you and your subconscious, which is your protection, is more keen.

Therefore, all your senses are sharper. This is very easy to prove with another simple example . . .

Imagine you are driving down a motorway, one you are very familiar with. You may start to go into a daydream, thinking about what you will be doing when you get to your destination. You go into a sort of autopilot, oblivious to your surroundings. You can be in this state of daydream for a few minutes. When your conscious comes out of this trance-type state, you may realise that you haven't even noticed the scenery or what other traffic is on the road. Perhaps you have a quick glance around to see if there are any police cars about and that you are not speeding. You may even think that if you had not come out of this state you could have had an accident.

In fact, when your conscious is occupied in this state of trance, the subconscious part of your mind comes forward as a protection mechanism. It sharpens your senses so that they are more aware. Even though your eyes may be glazed, if the car in front of you had put its brake lights on suddenly while you were in your daydream, your subconscious would immediately spring into action and alert your conscious. In that split second, your conscious would be in control and dealing with the situation. That is, you would quickly react and apply your own brakes to deal with the situation.

To continue the analogy, suppose there was an unusual smell in the car that may be attributed to the engine. Again, your subconscious would alert your conscious mind and you would instantly deal with the problem. Your subconscious is so sophisticated that if this was just a strange smell not associated with any possible danger, it would be ignored and you would stay in your day-dream. The same applies to hearing – if there was a strange, 'wrong' sound, your subconscious would interrupt your daydream and your conscious would check out the problem.

If you are not a driver, a better simile would probably be to imagine you are on a tube or train and you have some distance still to travel. You are deep in thought and concentrating on your daydreams. It is unlikely you will notice people getting on and off the tube, as you are so focused on your thoughts. But if there was a peculiar or threatening noise nearby, you would immediately come out of your trance state and check the source of the noise. This is your natural protection coming into play again. Your subconscious is a kind of 'guardian angel',allowing you to be in a daydream with comparative safety.

This incredibly sophisticated program we take for granted and don't even notice it exists, but it is the very essence of hypnosis. When you are in hypnosis you are protected by this very program and, so, if anything untoward happens while you are in the daydream state, then because your senses are so keen you will immediately terminate the trance, just as you did on the motorway or the tube train.

Is hypnosis dangerous?

Is *living* dangerous? I have never heard of anyone dying while in hypnosis. Yes, you can be conned in hypnosis –

but you don't need to be in hypnosis to have that happen to you! We have all seen stage shows in which people volunteer to go up and make fools of themselves. But when you go on the stage you are accepting responsibility – you are entering into a sort of contract with the hypnotist. If you know the hypnotist makes people perform silly and ridiculous antics, then why are you setting yourself up to be in the same position, unless you are a masochist?

But if you have seen an enjoyable hypnotic show and are willing to offer yourself as a participant, then there is no problem. People who go on stage at such shows are invariably exhibitionists who, either consciously or subconsciously, actually want to perform. If suddenly the act changed and became unsuitable to you, or you were being instructed to do something which you found too embarrassing or distasteful, then you would just bring yourself out of hypnosis, just as you would if you were in a daydream.

I know, because I have done just that. However, because I came out of hypnosis when I didn't want to do what I was asked, it didn't stop me from being re-hypnotised by the same stage hypnotist and persuaded to do other antics. In fact, I can say I thoroughly enjoyed the experience.

I had been a professional hypnotherapist for many years before I was myself hypnotised for a stage show. There are many hypnotherapists who loathe stage hypnotism because they feel it degrades their profession. However, I simply regard it as a different aspect of hypnosis and all I can say to them is, 'Don't knock it until you've tried it.'

Does everything I've said so far apply to self-hypnosis?

Since the hypnotic state is attained by suggestions while you are in the normal conscious state, then you are able to do this yourself in the form of self-hypnosis. The only difference is that a therapist will keep in check your relaxation, following your progress. When you practise hypnosis yourself you have to take this responsibility on your own shoulders, so a little commitment is important. The commitment is simply to concentrate and make sure you aren't going to be disturbed and that you are settled and comfortable. To be in the right temperature is also important, not too cold or not too warm. A little common sense is all that is needed. I will be telling you a lot more about self-hypnosis later.

How does hypnosis work?

As I said earlier, hypnosis is not sleep; in fact, it has no mental resemblance to sleep. If you are asleep, you cannot be in hypnosis. Unfortunately, the word 'hypnosis' was derived from the Greek word meaning 'sleep' and, therefore, this misinterpretation, coupled with the fact that the subject gives a physical resemblance of being in deep sleep, has resulted in a major world-wide misunderstanding of the whole science of the hypnotic trance.

You are always aware of what is being said and you always have a lazy form of control. Your control is to say 'No' if you do not like what is going on. You can simply terminate the hypnotic daydream state by just opening your eyes. Your mind has a safety device which will not take on board suggestions that you do not want to accept.

The information that you want is edited from the suggestions by your conscious mind. That is why if there is a trauma, then you need to satisfy the conscious to change its editing system. But if you are in a vulnerable position, because you are ill or in a very depressed state, your mind is more susceptible to persuasion in hypnosis, due to the fact of this vulnerability. But you can still call a halt and terminate the trance.

Just to return to my observations about stage hypnotism, you may at this point ask why people who participate seem to be in the hypnotist's control. Stage hypnosis has a different set of rules. You have already made the decision to allow yourself to be persuaded to perform apparently silly antics by agreeing to go on stage. It's a bit like letting the door-to-door salesman into your home. You are subconsciously saying, 'OK, try and sell me your goods and if I like what you've got to offer I'll buy.' This is all the salesman needs – a chance to pitch. In his mind he has already sold to the person the moment he is allowed to enter their house.

When on stage you have allowed your subconscious a free hand to play a game and it takes advantage of this freedom. If you were adamant on not being persuaded to respond, you would not be talked into going on the stage, just as if you were adamant about not buying from the salesman you wouldn't let him into your home in the first place.

Will I feel different?

This is another common misunderstanding. People believe that they will feel differently when they are in the hypnotic state – either that they will be unconscious, emerge from it not remembering anything or have a feeling of being controlled. But there is no feeling in hypnosis. In fact, the person who comes out of hypnosis for the first time will usually say, 'I wasn't hypnotised.'

If they do feel any of the above-mentioned feelings, then it is only because they expected to or if, say, they took on a hypnotic suggestion to feel a sensation, such as a tingling. The mind works to a basic set of rules and one of them says this – *what the mind expects tends to happen.*

Whether or not the person has any feeling in hypnosis has no bearing on the therapy work being done. The only advantage a feeling in hypnosis has is that it builds the belief system and the suggestions may be more effective. If a person has a fear of hypnosis because of ignorance, then this fear will terminate the hypnosis, anyway. He or she will have to get over this fear in order to be able to relax enough to go into hypnosis. An experienced therapist will be able to deal with this easily, although this fear is more than likely only to occur when with an experienced hypnotist. In self-hypnosis, that is working by yourself, rather than being guided into hypnosis by a therapist, then you know you have control.

So, you should just allow yourself to relax and drift into hypnosis, not fighting it or worrying when you reach the state. Accept it, expect it and it will happen. Follow the carefully prepared instructions, then you have a wonderful chance to work on yourself in the most natural way known to mankind – by using your brain.

Solving problems with hypnosis

People suffer symptoms when they have problems. The symptoms may have little to do with the cause and can lead the experts in the wrong direction. For example, over-eating may be a symptom of a trauma caused by a feeling of inferiority, due to constant character assassination by a parent or an authoritative person. Repetition of statements such as, 'If you don't do your work you will never amount to anything,' are an instance of this kind of thing. Or, 'You take everything for granted, you're just a slob and you'll never change.'

Sometimes, remarks like this can be repeated over and over again without any permanent damage or effect and in some cases can even enthuse the child to prove the instigator wrong. But, in general, this is a very negative and unhealthy environment for a young person, especially if this type of remark is said during the time of an awful trauma, while the child is vulnerable or in a state of deep shock.

Then, these negative responses can be far more damaging. They may be assumed by the subconscious as fact, rather than a possibility, without the usual editing. The logic of the conscious, which would be the normal, protective program, is bypassed. A new program is ready to be set into motion – a program for failure.

In shock, the conscious has crashed, rather like a

23

computer occasionally crashes, to use the analogy again. It has stopped working for a second or two. This is why at accident scenes it is imperative never to program the victim for death with chance remarks like, 'He'll never make it,' or 'She'll lose her legs, what a mess.' Medical staff are aware of these dangers and they are trained to soothe and say that everything is going to be fine, in order to prevent the victim going into shock.

Sometimes, this new program may not be put into practice until many years later. It may be triggered by a similar trauma to the original one. Confused? Well, you would be, if reading this book is your first introduction to hypnosis. It will come as a whole new science to you, incredibly simple, really, but only when you learn a new logic – a logic of the inner mind which is alien to normal, conscious behaviour. In fact, anything goes.

Contrary to popular belief, when you are in hypnosis you are not being controlled. Your will hasn't been taken away. Moreover, you can be intelligent and still be hypnotised. In fact, the more intelligent you are, usually the quicker it is for a well-trained therapist to work with you. Your intellect will accept the simple methods, realising the subtle sophistication behind a good therapy structure. So the key to good hypnosis is a good technique.

If you hear someone say, 'I've been to a hypnotherapist and it didn't work,' that is rather like saying, 'I've been to school and it didn't work because I didn't pass my exams.' It all depends on the training the therapist has had. A badly trained therapist will have difficulties when practising hypnosis.

Now, how does that affect you as far as self-hypnosis is concerned?

The formula is the same. You need good training and this book has been created to help you achieve just that. The scripts that you will use to induce hypnosis and the scripts that you employ to entice the new, favoured behaviour are supplied for you. All you need to practise at is to read them evenly and smoothly into a tape recorder. The most professional hypnotherapist in the world has to communicate the correct words. Knowing the correct words are the fruits of his or her training. Remember, words are your tools. Words change an attitude and a change of attitude results in a change of behaviour.

2

HOW TO USE SELF-HYPNOSIS

A quick but thorough instruction into the basics.

In order to be able to undertake the simplest tasks in self-hypnosis, such as the suggestion hypnosis through which you will be taught to effect the change in your eating habits, it is helpful to have a full understanding of how it works. Because this can give a better success rate to your self-help therapy, I have divided this section of the book into two parts. The first part, in this chapter, explains how self-hypnosis – which you will be using to operate the concept of Slim While You Sleep – works, and the second part, which you will find in the following chapter, comprises the actual instructions.

All hypnosis is self-hypnosis but generally when we talk about self-hypnosis we are discussing how someone puts themselves into hypnosis without the aid of another person to guide them. The hypnotherapist is simply a guide who helps the subject into hypnosis and is not indispensable – but with his or her help the subject will be more likely to enter into a good, deep trance state quickly and easily.

The professional stage hypnotist has developed certain inductions – an induction is the set of words used to induce a hypnotic trance – that put a person instantly into hypnosis. It takes only seconds and can look very dramatic. But these techniques are not one hundred per cent reliable and are generally only successful on very suggestible people, who on average constitute approximately a third of any given audience. The stage hypnotist is particularly experienced in such instant induction techniques because time is of the essence in the act, otherwise the audience will very quickly get bored and restless.

On the other hand, the hypnotherapist has the luxury of time and can chose the induction he or she prefers, whether it be rapid and immediate or slow and relaxing. Most practitioners will more likely take the slower approach, considering they will be treating a cross-section of both the susceptible and the not-so-susceptible subjects. Hypnotherapists know that everyone can be induced into hypnosis by one technique or another and would rather be sure of good hypnosis with the slow technique than chance losing their subject's belief structure at the beginning of therapy with the not-as-successful rapid or instant techniques.

At one time in the experimental stages, as far back as the 1840s, the surgeon James Esdaile, an early pioneer who carried out more than 2,000 operations using hypnosis, would take up to an hour and a half to induce deep trance for anaesthesia. The modern hypnotherapist with a little more understanding of how the mind works has been able to speed up the inductions and has a choice of three types, ranging from seconds to twenty minutes, depending on preference. So really we are dealing with percentages when we talk of inductions. The instant induction needs a very confident hypnotist and a suggestible subject. The rapid induction works on a larger percentage of people, while the progressive, slow method is far more reliable for the majority of subjects.

The stage hypnotist knows he will be able to work with approximately one third of the audience using instant inductions. The hypnotherapist knows he or she can work with every subject as long as the necessary time is spent with each individual. However, self-hypnosis has a lot of hurdles to get over which, if not adequately prepared for, prevent some subjects feeling any relaxation at all from whatever induction they use. So, we have to prepare for the obstacles and, to this end, an understanding of how the mind works will be of great benefit to the person who may find, or has found, it difficult to go into hypnosis.

The very first thing you will find if you are new to hypnosis, as explained in Chapter 1, is that there is no feeling in it, just as there is no feeling when you go into a daydream. People going into hypnosis for the first time expect to feel *different* in some way – which often accounts for their extreme nervousness about it. So how do you know when you are hypnotised? *The fact is you don't*.

You may have seen people on a stage hypnotist's show performing extraordinary tasks and when they are brought out of their trance refusing to believe they were in hypnosis at all. Just as the alcoholic has to admit he is an alcoholic before he can be treated, the person who is going to practise self-hypnosis needs to accept that it is unlikely that he or she will have any feelings in hypnosis except that of peacefulness and relaxation. The exception is when the subconscious may have taken a suggestion on board from something read earlier or spoken about hypnosis, indicating there may be a feeling or tingling sensation. The subject may not have any memory of hearing this information but it presents itself when they are hypnotised and they experience a tingling sensation because they have been told earlier that they will.

It was common practice for a hypnotist to suggest this to a subject as a suggestibility test. The subject who said they felt a slight tingling had accepted the suggestion and therefore was suggestible. The person feeling nothing had not accepted the suggestion but could still be experiencing the same quality of hypnosis.

The power of suggestion

I want to begin by explaining in detail the different stages of trance, so that you have a better understanding of what is happening to subjects when they are experiencing hypnosis. For suggestion hypnosis, any of these stages is adequate. It is only when you require the subject to participate in the therapy, either by answering a question or making a physical movement – for example, by lifting an arm – that if they haven't responded you should know why. It was only ignorance that caused fear of hypnosis in the first place and it's only ignorance that still fuels that fear today. All trance state is hypnosis but there are different stages of trance, encouraging a different set of responses. For explanation purposes, I have called the stages 'depths'. I am purposely leaving out scientific theories and just presenting easy-to-understand facts.

1 The light trance

The light trance is when the mind and body are relaxed. Relaxed enough to slow the mind down so that it can focus in imagination clearly. In this form of trance you can work easily with both suggestion and more advanced therapy; you can even achieve partial amnesia, which is excellent for accelerated learning. Your conscious isn't battling with the new material, logically analysing the new information. The conscious sits back and allows this fresh data to flow through as it would through a four-year-old. There are certain physical changes that occur when a person is in hypnosis, such as eyelids fluttering rapidly and droopiness of the face, as in sleep. If you instruct the client to open their eyes, the whites can look very pink for a second or so, due to the eye muscles relaxing. There is a list of such signs but because they can be very misleading and the subject may not show any noticeable symptom whilst still in deep hypnosis, I have just briefly mentioned them so you are aware of their existence.

2 Somnambulism

The phenomenon of somnambulism, a deeper trance, was discovered by a student of Mesmer in the 1800s, Count

Maxime de Puysegut. The mind is completely relaxed, either by a group of instructions in the form of a suggestion or occasionally some subjects go directly into this state spontaneously. To achieve this state by suggestion, the semantics used are very important and need to be consistent. The word, somnambulism, in hypnosis terms shouldn't be confused with the dictionary explanation, which is sleep walking.

The stage hypnotist relies on this depth of hypnosis, as the subject can talk, open their eyes and still carry out tasks. It is also called 'waking' hypnosis. A popular demonstration to prove the phenomenon of trance is to ask a hypnotised subject to pick a number between one and ten, then instruct them to eliminate it from their memory and forget this instruction. The subconscious will do this as it holds no threat to the person involved. It would not act on an instruction that would either lead to embarrassment or be harmful to the subject's individual standards.

The suggestions given when the subject is in somnambulism show how the mind can follow outside influence, in this case causing partial amnesia. When the subject is asked to open their eyes, they are then instructed to count their fingers. Invariably, they miss the number they have been asked to forget and end up with one finger spare. They looked totally bemused, not knowing how they have managed to miscalculate!

3 The 'coma' trance
The coma state is a much deeper state of hypnosis still. It is the only state in which the subject is catatonic. This means

you can move the subject's arm into any position, however uncomfortable it may look, and it will stay there until you move it again. The limb feels waxy, more pliable. The subject experiences lethargy and is completely and wonderfully relaxed, their whole body being fully anaesthetised.

The coma state, unless being used for painless surgery, is of little use in advanced forms of hypnotherapy because the subject will not respond to physical suggestions or be able to answer questions. To the stage hypnotist it is a menace. Because it is such a marvellously relaxing state for the subject, they simply do not want to be disturbed! Before it was discovered how to terminate this trance, the hypnotist would try and get the subject off the stage as soon as possible – usually failing to arouse the person, which would upset and worry the audience.

Although very uncommon and most unlikely, it is possible that a subject can go directly into the coma state immediately they are hypnotised. This state is the origin of the old fear – and total myth – that a subject could be 'stuck' in hypnosis. If left alone, subjects will bring themselves out of the trance, just as they would if they were daydreaming. It is no more harmful than that.

Whenever people who are ignorant about hypnosis express this fear to me, I always reply: 'Where do they keep these people who are stuck for ever in hypnosis? Show them to me!' The most successful suggestion to terminate this type of trance is to issue a kind of mild threat by saying to the subject: 'If you don't come out of hypnosis now, you will never be able to go into it again.' Because it is such a pleasant and enjoyable state, the thought of never being able to enter hypnosis again always brings the subject out of their trance.

So how do you hypnotise yourself?

There are three basic types of inductions used to relax a person into hypnosis. They consist of (a) shock, (b) confusion and (c) boredom. The instant induction, which has a shock element and is immediate in its effect, looks very impressive for demonstrations, taking only seconds to induce full relaxation. The rapid induction, which basically confuses the mind by overloading it, presents a more gentle approach but still takes less than a minute to induce. The progressive induction really bores the mind into hypnosis. The latter is considered the most reliable and is the method most usually used for self-hypnosis. This traditional, progressive method can take quite some time – the longest one illustrated in this book takes approximately twelve minutes.

TECHNIQUE FOR SELF-HYPNOSIS IN STAGES
1   An Understanding of the Method
2   Progressive Relaxation
3   Deepeners
4   Instruction into Self-hypnosis
5   Rehearsal in Hypnosis
6   Counting out of Hypnosis
7   Ask the Subject to Practise Method
8   Check the Practice is Satisfactory

The instructions that follow are for the volunteer who is guiding another person into hypnosis. If you don't have a volunteer, then follow the above instructions but tape your own voice on a tape recorder and play it back when you are sitting or lying down comfortably. I have purposely excluded instructions for the instant and rapid inductions because they are more advanced techniques, but I have introduced them to you so you are aware they exist.

The three types of inductions

The instant induction: this is used mainly in the USA and is quite spectacular when exhibited publicly. It consists of confusion, shock and aggression. This can be used on anyone. One very famous American hypnotist has a technique of grasping the subject by the back of the head and seeming to pulling the head sharply downwards on to his shoulder, while at the same moment issuing the one-word command, 'Sleep!' In fact, he doesn't exert any pressure – the subject's head just drops on to the hypnotist's shoulder.

The subject may look as if they have gone into a faint and sometimes have to be laid down full length on the floor. In fact, they are fully aware and find it pleasant and relaxing. It is quite extraordinary to witness for the first time and is very effective, showing the power of suggestion at its best. If a person has experienced a severe trauma or scare, they will be automatically in hypnosis. The conscious stops processing and the subconscious is vulnerable. This type of induction obviously needs another person to do the hypnosis.

The rapid induction: Dave Elman, a modern master of hypnosis, developed what I believe to be the most successful technique of rapid induction, which uses confusion and complicated short instructions to close down the conscious part of the mind, exposing the subconscious. It is very effective and this type of induction is useful for inducing hypnosis when a person has already had previous experience of being hypnotised. This induction also needs another person to perform the actual hypnosis, unless the subject is already in shock.

The progressive induction: this is the most important and simple induction to use and in practical terms the only one that is ideal for self-hypnosis. The words are what guide the subject into hypnosis. Therefore, it can be induced via a person, cassette tapes or videos. You don't have to have another person present to guide you into hypnosis – you can just listen to a pre-recording, either bought or prepared by yourself.

It is just an exercise into relaxation with many different words to entice a reaction and participation; for example, the words may suggest 'tighten the muscles in your feet'. The instruction occupies the conscious while relaxing the mind, allowing the suggestion to be accepted. As the instructions become monotonous, the mind relaxes even more.

It is literally 'boring' the person into hypnosis. Because it is more effective to have at least a modicum of attention while inducing the relaxation, it is better to have a script which employs varied words. It is not as effective if you keep using the same verb continuously in the instructions, such as 'Tighten the muscles in your feet, now relax those muscles. Now tighten the muscles in your calves . . . now begin to relax the muscles. Tighten the muscles in your thighs, now begin to relax those long muscles.'

There are exceptions in certain words that may be used continually to join the suggestion together, such as 'Now', and 'And', which can be used liberally, or powerful words such as 'Down', which are used repetitively when leading the subject deeper into trance. This is the only method where the subject has no need for another person to lead them – it can be taped.

The progressive relaxation technique gradually slows down the metabolism of the client and so, however stressed or tense they may be at the beginning, eventually this technique will guide them into deep relaxation. The technique ensures a relaxation that is adequate to be followed by the appropriate suggestion and, as long as the problem isn't trauma-based and is in the subject's interest, the subconscious will accept the new program.

You can prevent yourself going into hypnosis by refusing to relax, otherwise there is no reason that the suggestion shouldn't work. Don't spend time on worrying whether you are achieving hypnosis. Just let your mind drift with the words and it will happen.

First, you must accept that you can be hypnotised, that it is nothing to do with intelligence or willpower – it is a fact that we can all hypnotise ourselves. And if you are not attaining it, then it's your responsibility. Like anything else, practice makes perfect. In order to have good self-hypnosis,

I would suggest that the very first time you try it you get yourself a volunteer to help guide you with the instructions given. Then, when you have been guided successfully into trance, it will be much easier for you to do it yourself subsequently.

To help you understand the initial difficulties you may face, I would like you to imagine that you are a native of Barbados and that you are watching television. You have never experienced severe cold or touched snow. There is a film on TV showing a group of people stranded in a snow storm; their car has broken down and they are suffering with severe cold and experiencing frostbite because they are not prepared or dressed properly and so are exposed to the elements. If you had never experienced the cold of a snow storm, it would be impossible for someone to explain it so that you could actually feel it, to experience the extreme cold these stranded people were feeling.

If you were then taken to Britain and experienced a cold day, this still would not give you a real insight into what the snow actually feels like and how cold it can become in a blizzard. But if you were taken to the Arctic in a blizzard and had first-hand experience of what this type of cold is like in relation to the cold you had already been subjected to, when you returned to Barbados and saw a television picture of a snow storm you would know exactly how it felt and you might even spontaneously shiver with just the thought of it. Once your mind has experienced a feeling, it is permanently stored in the memory banks and that memory can immediately remind you of the real experience. A favourite song can bring sadness or joy and a particular smell can also awaken a memory in a split second.

If you relate this analogy to hypnosis, the stage hypnotist has taken you to the Arctic blizzard. The hypnotherapist, depending on how good a hypnotist he or she is or, even more important, how good the script is, will decide whether you experience the blizzard or just a cold day in the UK. But with self-hypnosis you may just try it yourself with your own mind meditation or a selection of the many cassette tape recordings or videos on the market, so you chance not getting anywhere, like the native in Barbados watching the snow blizzard trying to figure out what all the fuss is about and having no idea what it feels like to be really cold. If you approach self-hypnosis knowing what to expect – or rather what not to expect – with practice and perseverance there is no reason why you can't use this incredible control of your own mind to change your attitudes and personality defects. *It is that powerful.*

Also, when you have been led to experience self-hypnosis you can easily attain it yourself if you have been given some good instructions and methods to help you, especially if this includes a post-hypnotic suggestion. This is a suggestion in the form of an instruction to be acted on when the subject has terminated their trance. It is powerful and remarkable. The subconscious activates the instruction without the subject's conscious being aware that the suggestion was ever made in the first place. The post-hypnotic suggestion is given when the subject is actually in hypnosis.

But even with the extra help of a post-hypnotic suggestion you need to practise self-hypnosis continually. If you don't, then, as the old saying goes, 'What you don't use, you lose!'. You may think you can't win but the reason why so many people are disappointed with pre-recorded self-hypnosis tapes or videos is because they expect to feel different when they are hypnotised, even to the extent of expecting to be in a coma-type state. Once you have been hypnotised, the tapes and videos can be very beneficial, although no more so than creating your own tape recordings from something as simple as a pocket recorder and creating your own personal scripts from the rules for suggestions on page 44.

There are four methods by which you can attain self-hypnosis. I have listed them below, each with their advantages and disadvantages. There is no question about it – for speed and depth of trance, it is to your advantage to have someone to help guide you through your first hypnotic experience.

Method one

Using a volunteer to guide you into hypnosis. The advantages are that the volunteer can be instructed by the book and if he or she follows the instructions carefully they will induce good, deep hypnosis. In order to produce a deep trance all you need is suggestion hypnosis. That is to say that anyone you feel comfortable with can read the words and you will go into hypnosis.

Disadvantage: you must be careful about selecting a

volunteer with the right attitude. A giggler or an unconfident stutterer would be very distracting.

Method two

Using a tape recording or video to induce self-hypnosis. Because you can easily be distracted even when there is no-one there, such as by the phone ringing, keeping your mind busy with daily routines or planning what you will be having for dinner instead of listening or watching the tape, you may find it difficult to relax enough for a good deep trance, but if you persist you will certainly go into some sort of relaxation.

Disadvantage: you don't have someone to guide you and use deepeners that encourage a much deeper state of trance. You don't have someone there to pace the hypnosis to your individual thoughts. Videos and tapes do not take into account something that may distract you and so you can easily become out of sync with the induction at the beginning stages of hypnosis. Struggling and worrying that you can't catch up interferes with the relaxation and chances of hypnosis.

Method three

Using an experienced hypnotherapist to induce hypnosis. The advantage is that the hypnotherapist will have the expertise to sound confident, although he or she will only be following scripts similar to those illustrated in this book. There is no reason why the volunteer cannot induce the same quality of hypnosis by themselves. For suggestion hypnosis only, an experienced hypnotherapist is not a necessity. For advanced techniques, then an experienced hypnotherapist is essential. Not because it is dangerous – it isn't – but mainly because without the experience it will be difficult for the lone person to work with the same efficiency and ease that comes with a good training background.

I have trained hypnotherapists in workshops who have read every conceivable book on the workings of hypnosis and who, before the course, did not have the confidence to carry out the advanced techniques necessary to create a change of behaviour in their clients. After the all-important one-to-one training, their confidence was established. For a student to try and learn advanced techniques in hypnosis from books alone is like going for a solo flight in a light aircraft without having any previous one-to-one training or even, for that matter, sitting in an aircraft cockpit before the flight. It can be done, but it takes absolute confidence and guts and when it comes to the crunch not everyone is cut out for it. So, you tend to find a lot of hypnotherapists who, rather than train at established courses, choose the easy way out and stick to suggestion therapy only.

Disadvantage: using an experienced hypnotherapist to employ suggestion hypnosis only can be expensive. It will cost you anything between £25 and £150 per session and he or she will only be working with a similar script to those that can be found in the following chapters. Anyone who can read the appropriate scripts in a confident and easy manner can attain the same level of hypnosis as the professional hypnotherapist but without the extra cost.

Method four

Instruction with groups. This is quite popular and ranges from half-day to weekend courses. This, of course, depends on the technique used and the instruction.

Disadvantage: sometimes costly and not always effective.

Of the three methods of induction, we will be concentrating on the progressive. The other two are more for advanced techniques and have no extra benefits apart from the time element. I have included two basic scripts for progressive inductions. If you decide to practise self-hypnosis without the assistance of an experienced therapist, using a volunteer to do the induction or taping it yourself, the progressive induction is a must. So I will be concentrating on this particular technique.

The progressive induction

You can choose scripts that take you by the sea, into a garden, on a boat or on a magical journey. The list is endless but do remember that a percentage of people have a fear of drowning and, therefore, would not find scripts involving water very relaxing. Personally, I find the garden satisfies virtually everyone.

To help you read aloud the script with the correct

pauses, I have purposely exaggerated the spacing. It is also important to realise that it is one of those rare instances where the grammar does not have to be so precise. In fact, it may be not only acceptable but to your advantage if the words are not arranged with complete accuracy, as this causes a controlled confusion of the subject's mind, leading him or her more easily into relaxation.

Progressive relaxation induction script

'I want you to imagine that you're checking your body to ensure you become totally relaxed . . . As your muscles relax, just let your mind relax also . . . begin with your feet . . . feel your toes . . . stretch them, feel the texture of what your feet are resting on . . . begin to tighten your calves . . . now relax them . . . let that relaxation spread past your ankles, up your calves to the back of the knee . . . feel those muscles easing . . . resting comfortably . . . now your thighs, pull them tight . . . be aware of those long muscles tensing . . . now relax those muscles, feel them lengthening and resting comfortably . . . feel your legs as they sink even deeper into the cushions as you relax even more . . . now your stomach muscles, pull them together gently . . . now let them expand and relax comfortably.

'Your shoulders and back muscles . . . flex your shoulders . . . feel those muscles pull across your back . . . now let your shoulders slouch as you relax the muscles . . . and notice how your spine sinks deeper into your chair as you relax even more deeply.

'Notice how easy and regular your breathing has become . . . now your fingertips and fingers, clench them, feel that tension . . . now relax them . . . and allow the relaxation to spread up your arms to your neck . . . make sure your neck is comfortable with your head in an easy position . . . tighten up your neck muscles . . . now let them loosen up, as the muscles relax allow your neck to sink back into a comfortable position.

'Your face muscles are flat and stretch comfortably across your face . . . squeeze up your face . . . and feel the tension . . . now relax those muscles and feel them lengthening and softening, relax more than ever before.

'You can now feel the air temperature against your skin . . . It feels smooth and comfortable . . . now you can allow the relaxation to spread to your scalp, knowing that you are relaxed throughout your body from the top of your head to the tips of your toes.

'Your body is now loose . . . and limp . . . and heavy . . . and relaxed . . . notice how your body is sinking deeper into relaxation . . . as your breathing becomes more regular and easy . . . in a moment I will count slowly from one . . . to ten . . . and with each number you drift deeper and deeper into peaceful relaxation . . . 1 . . . 2 . . . 3 . . . 4 . . . 5 . . . 6 . . . 7 . . . 8 . . . 9 . . . 10. [Count slowly and deliberately.]

'You are now feeling so deeply relaxed . . . you find it easy to focus your attention, and image things very clearly . . . and I want you to imagine that you are standing on a balcony which has steps leading down to a beautiful garden . . . as you look into the garden . . . you see that it

45

is surrounded with lovely trees, ensuring the garden is private, secluded and peaceful. There are flower beds set in the lovely lawn and further along is a waterfall flowing into a stream. Listen to the sound of the water . . . as you look around, you see the trees and you hear a faint sound of a bird in the distance . . . adding to the feeling of deep relaxation through your entire being. If you look more closely you will see that there are five steps leading down to the garden and then a small path that leads to the waterfall . . . in a moment we will walk down the steps and with each step you go deeper and deeper into relaxation. So let's begin . . .

'Watch your foot as you place it on to the first step . . . and as you do this you feel yourself going deeper into relaxation. [As you lead your subject down the steps, you find you can slow down the rhythm of their breathing by slowing down the pace of the descent.]

'Down on to the second step and as you feel your foot firmly placed on the step you feel a wonderful relief as you drift even deeper into relaxation . . . down on to the third step, feeling wonderfully free and . . . so . . . so . . . relaxed . . . as your foot reaches for the fourth step another wave of relaxation drifts through your whole body . . . down on to the fifth step now and feeling even more deeply relaxed than ever before.

'Now you are standing on the lawn, you see a little way ahead is the waterfall and at the side of it is a garden bench . . . notice the colour of the bench . . . what it is made of. [If this is being read, add 'say "yes" when you see the bench in your mind'. Also make sure you have done the visual *test on page 52 before the hypnosis.]*

*'In a moment I would like you to walk over to the bench
. . . and sit down on the bench . . . When you sit down
you will be surprised at how comfortable it is . . . and
then you will be even more relaxed than you are now . . .
so let's begin to walk over . . . now sit down on the bench
. . . As you sit down on the bench, take a deep breath . . .
and as you breathe out you feel a wave of relaxation go
through your body relaxing every muscle and nerve . . .
[stay silent for the count of three seconds] . . . as you
breathe in . . . you breathe in positive thoughts . . . and as
you breathe out . . . you breathe out negative thoughts . . .
leaving room for more positive thoughts.'*

The above induction should be followed by the self-
hypnosis instruction or a suggestion that is appropriate. If
your subject just wants to experience hypnosis, the 'ego'
suggestion should be added. It would be a shame to waste
a chance to give a positive suggestion.

For self-hypnosis instruction, the progressive should be
followed by one of the deepeners below. I favour the fantasy
garden but either the ruler or the lift is just as satisfactory.

To deepen the level of hypnosis an extra script is used
when the subject is in hypnosis.

Deepeners

What is a deepener?

A deepener is a suggestion given while the subject is in
hypnosis for the purpose of attaining a deeper trance. The

words used suggest that you will go deeper into hypnosis and various exercises allow the imagination to take the mind to an even deeper level of relaxation. The purpose of this is so the subject can completely relax, slowing down conscious thoughts, allowing suggestions to be accepted easily without too much interference from the logical, conscious part of the mind.

The deep trance does not have many benefits in therapy, apart from when a patient needs to be anaesthetised. It is a wonderful feeling to attain this state in self-hypnosis, very comforting and secure. It also helps you to focus your imagination better.

What is the purpose of a deepener?

The main purpose of a deepener is to guide the subject into a feeling of concentrated pure relaxation and an added advantage is to show them how they are able to adjust the level themselves.

How to use a deepener

There are four examples of deepeners listed below which have been used and tested for many years in relaxation techniques. While a person is in hypnosis, because of the subconscious being accessible, any instruction can be used as a deepener. The instruction bypasses the conscious and the subconscious follows the directions of the suggestion. Literally any instructions, followed by the words, 'and you will be five times more relaxed' or 'and then you will be doubly relaxed' when the instructions are performed, then the action itself acts as a deepener.

The stage hypnotist uses this technique to both entertain and deepen. He may say: 'When I touch my ear you will go into a deep sleep,' and the subject immediately mimics a deep sleep. In fact, they are aware of everything going on but the subconscious is now in charge. It takes words literally and, so, is very precise in the actions it performs. If the subconscious is requested – which can happen with stage hypnosis – to act like a chicken, the subconscious will go into the memory banks and the person concerned will do an excellent imitation of a chicken. The subject would be far too inhibited to do this consciously, to act so well. Also, the memory files which incite such a brilliant performance aren't accessible to the conscious

Therefore, when the hypnotist touches his ear the subject goes directly into what looks like a deep sleep. The subconscious has accepted the instruction and followed it without the participant being aware of consciously no longer being in control. Remember, the stage hypnotist has checked his audience for suggestibility at this point and will only use the ones in the audience that are very suggestible, simply for speed and entertainment value.

The hypnotherapist will use a deepener to help his or her subject into deep relaxation so as to enable the subject to experience a sense of total calm. This can be especially effective with high-powered business people.

An example of a simple deepener would be to say: *'In a moment when I snap my fingers you will be doubly relaxed.'* Or: *'When I drop your arm into your lap you'll be five times more relaxed'*.

Another popular deepener could be in the form of a story. Four examples are given below.

The lift

This is an old favourite that has been used for years. I used it for the first few years of my practice but later preferred the ruler or the steps into paradise.

'*I would like you to come with me into a lift . . . the doors are opening and you step inside . . . it is roomy and feels comfortable . . . look around the lift . . . it's a very special lift . . . notice the colour of the surroundings . . . a comfortable soft colour that reassures you . . . From the panel on one side of the doors that are now closing, you notice that we are on the third floor . . . you look at the panel again and see that the lift is going down to the second floor . . . look . . . it has now reached the floor and the lift door opens . . . but you do not want to get out because you know you can go deeper into the basement of relaxation . . . so look for the button that says Floor One . . . When you are ready press that button that says One . . . We now start to drift . . . floating down to the basement of relaxation . . . So look for the button that says B . . . Press the button and notice that the lift goes down . . . and down . . . by passing the first floor . . . and deeper and deeper . . . down to the very basement of relaxation. Down . . . down . . . now you are at the basement . . . So relaxed . . . so calm . . . so free . . . The doors open and you walk out into a wonderful luxurious comfortable place . . . There's a chair that looks so relaxing . . . you walk over to sit on the chair . . .*

knowing you will sink into the cushions . . . and as you do so, you experience a marvellous feeling of pure peace of mind and tranquillity.'

The ruler

This is a wonderful deepener, it allows the subject to have full control of their level of trance and is particularly useful for the person who has a fear of hypnosis.

'*What I would like you to do is imagine a three-foot ruler in front of you. This is a very special ruler because it measures relaxation. Can you see the ruler? [If this is being read aloud, add: 'Say "yes" when you see it.'] Good, what colour is it? Good.*

'*Now, if you look more closely you will see there are numbers on this ruler. At the very top you can see a number one and at the bottom you are surprised to see the number go right down to one hundred.*

'*In a few moments I will count from one to three and snap my fingers and when I do, a number will appear as if by magic. This number will tell you how relaxed you are. . . one . . . two . . . three [snap fingers]. What number do you see? . . . Good . . . Now take a deep breath, and every time I ask you to do this you will find that you become twice as relaxed as you are now. Taking another deep breath, breathe in. Good. Now breathe out slowly. What number is on your ruler now?*'

What is amazing about this ruler is you can actually determine your own relaxation by picking a number and going straight there. I will show you what I mean: '*What I want you to do is look at the ruler and go up to number five. Now go down to number ninety. Notice how deeply relaxed you feel as you drag your eyes down the ruler. Go down and down the ruler, pulling yourself into a wonderful deep peaceful feeling. Now come up the ruler and notice how lighter you feel as you float up.'* (At this point you can bring the subject out of hypnosis by counting them out or take them down to the basement and give them a suggestion.)

Visualisation deepener

This type of deepener is for people who can visualise easily.

'As you sit there enjoying the feeling of relaxation and allowing yourself to go easily and effortlessly into rest, I would like you to visualise yourself in a place that you have enjoyed visiting where you have felt happy, calm and relaxed . . . allow yourself to be in that place now . . . take in the security . . . Notice the colours around you . . . how bright . . . how dull . . . how soft . . . how pleasing.

'The atmosphere . . . notice if there is a breeze and whether there is sun or shade . . . as you allow yourself to remember this pleasant memory, so you go deeper and deeper into complete and utter rest.'

Steps into paradise

This deepener is my favourite to exercise depth in preparation for self-hypnosis. First you guide the subject on to their garden bench from the progressive relaxation, then continue with the deepener.

'As you are sitting comfortable you see a little way

*ahead ten steps that lead to a lower part of the garden . . .
and you can see just a few feet in front of the bottom step
a large heavy wooden door . . . set in an archway made out
of stone that leads to another part of the garden . . . you
don't know what it is like through the door but you have
this feeling that it is a wonderful peaceful place . . . you feel
the need to explore and so you decide to walk down the
steps . . . you know instinctively that each step will bring a
feeling of deep relaxation . . . you walk over to the top
steps and you begin to descend. On the first step a
wonderful feeling of relaxation comes over you . . . the next
step and you feel you are going deeper and deeper into
relaxation . . . down . . . to the third step, even deeper
relaxed . . . the fourth step, deeper still . . . down to the fifth
. . . the sixth . . . and the seventh . . . feeling deeper and
deeper relaxed . . . you are nearly at the bottom now . . .
the eighth step you are feeling so, so, relaxed . . . the ninth
and the tenth . . . you begin to walk over to the doorway
knowing that on the other side is the most beautiful place
. . . your special place . . . as you put your hand on the large
handle the door creaks open and you are confronted with
the most beautiful view.*

*'What makes this place so special is that you can add
whatever you like, whether it be mountains, sand or
flowers . . . you look around and you design your special
place . . . you know that this is the basement of your
relaxation and that you can come here at any time . . . to
address your subconscious or just to relax . . . You see a
comfortable place to sit. You can even lie down if you
wish . . . You walk over and make yourself comfortable*

and as you do . . . a feeling of pure peace of mind and a deep relaxation washes over you like a wave and both in your body and mind you are in complete harmony totally relaxed . . . as you relax your mind it re-energises itself, your body allowing your own healing forces to function.'

Once you have established a deep relaxed trance, the subject is now ready for the instructions for self-hypnosis with a post-hypnotic suggestion, instructions for the acting therapist to say when the induction and deepeners are completed (replacing the suggestion).

Post-hypnotic suggestion for self-hypnosis

I find this method most effective as an instruction. It has a jolt and trigger effect. This means that the instruction includes an action, for example, an arm dropping into the lap. The trigger of the drop or jolt keeps the conscious focused and occupied, allowing the suggestion of depth of trance to be accepted by the subconscious.

This is much more effective when a person has been in hypnosis a few times, taking care each time to use deepeners to increase the depth of relaxation. It is more beneficial to teach the subject self-hypnosis when they have been in hypnosis at least three times, each time being guided to a deeper level. Because the subject will normally only experience the depth in self-hypnosis they have been led to, if you were to do the self-hypnosis technique on the first occasion the subject will probably only feel a light form of relaxation – nothing so profound as when the trouble is taken to do the important preliminary exercises into deep trance.

This is the suggestion script: *'In a moment I will ask you to lift up your right arm and silently say the words, "I'm going into deep hypnosis now". As you say the word, "hypnosis", let your right arm drop into your lap and you will be even more deeply relaxed than you are now. Now go to your garden bench and bring out your ruler [or use the fantasy garden]. Check what level of relaxation you are in and then go down to the level you desire. If it is the basement level, say "basement". Before you go into self-hypnosis, give yourself a time limit and your body will automatically come out of this deep state at the time allotted. Your body has its own clock that keeps perfect time.'*

Ask the subject to rehearse it and then bring the subject out of hypnosis and ask them to practise in front of you. If the practice is done daily, by the end of the week you should be able just to image the actions by rehearsing them in the mind and after practising for a further week you will be able to do this without even closing their eyes. You should be able to put yourself into self-hypnosis on a bus, train or tube, etc.

It is important to establish that, like any habit, this needs continual practice. If you stop practising, then the level of relaxation will be lighter. But if kept up the advantages are tremendous and it only takes a couple of minutes daily.

Advantages of self-hypnosis

I will mention just four important obvious advantages, though there are many more.

1 A deep relaxation in body and mind can be a supplement to someone who is unable to enjoy their full quota of sleep. This method helps a person with insomnia and is more interesting than counting sheep.

2 It relieves stress immediately.

3 It can be used to access your own subconscious and discover information you may need to help break a bad habit, for example, 'Why am I doing this?' The reply will be the first answer from your subconscious, which will always be the correct one. If you don't like the answer, tough! A 'best of three'-type question and answer will not be appropriate! The first answer that simply pops into your mind from your subconscious is always the right one, the only one you should take notice of.

4 If you want to formulate a speech, you can access your subconscious to do so and leave it to do the work while you get on with something else. Your subconscious has the facility to do this but, unfortunately, we don't realise this and don't always trust our subconscious.

Attorneys in the USA are aware that they are using this facility in their courtroom addresses. They have to evaluate new information immediately and build it into their most important closing speech. This skill determines whether they are simply a good or a brilliant attorney and, while they may believe that it is their own skill that they are trusting, it is in fact their subconscious.

Accessing your subconscious in self-hypnosis

If you wish to ask questions of your subconscious while you are in self-hypnosis, when you reach your special place or basement of relaxation, image a TV screen about three feet high and ask questions into it. Imagine that the TV screen is your subconscious – whatever thought comes immediately into your mind, either on to the screen or just as a word, is the answer from your subconscious. Don't analyse the answer. At first, practise simple questions – 'Why am I having trouble sleeping?' or 'Why am I getting so many colds?' Learn to trust your subconscious.

Counting out of hypnosis

You can choose to count a subject out of hypnosis by using whatever combination of numbers you prefer. I like to count out from ten backwards to one.

'In a moment I will count from ten to one . . . and at the count of one you will open your eyes . . . and feel fully aware and enthusiastic . . . ten, nine, eight . . . coming up now . . . seven, six, five . . . more and more aware . . . four, three, two, one, eyes open.'

3

THE CONCEPT

A brand-new approach to slimming

Therapy work in hypnosis has generally been done while the client is in an altered state of awareness – a type of daydream, as I explained in Chapter 1 – but, nevertheless, awake. When you are in hypnosis, you are awake. If you are asleep, you are not in hypnosis. However deeply asleep you may look in hypnosis, you are still always aware of what is going on.

Suggestion hypnosis is just a specially adapted set of words, introduced while the subject is in hypnosis, that create a new program for the subconscious part of the mind to follow. This program brings about a permanent change in the subject, resulting in more favourable behaviour. However, things may be more complicated if there has been a trauma-related incident, directly responsible for and causing the previously unwanted behaviour. This trauma will either be forgotten or edited out by the subconscious and, therefore, prevent the conscious part of the mind being able to sort out the problem.

You may say: 'I don't want to eat but I cannot stop myself,' or 'I'm . . . (smoking/over-eating/drinking/gambling/losing my temper) . . . but I don't want to.' If you are doing something you don't want to do, but doing it anyway, then you are working from an out-of-date or incorrect program in your mind. This needs changing by either suggestion hypnosis or advanced methods of hypnotherapy which, for maximum effect, would normally include regression therapy. But now there is another option, a completely new concept – a new method which is so sophisticated it seems to work at a different level of intelligence that we, the professional hypnotherapists, were previously unaware of.

I am going to make a statement here which may seem contradictory at first but will become clear if you bear with me. It is very complicated, even for the advanced hypnotherapist, to put the client into Hypno-Sleep. But it is much simpler for subjects to achieve it by themselves!

What is Hypno-Sleep? Hypno-Sleep is a term coined by the American pioneer in this therapy, Jack Mason, whose details you will find in the useful addresses section at the back of the book. It is virtually unknown in this country but Jack, generous man that he is, has allowed me to be his disciple and promote the technique in the UK. Hypno-Sleep is a different state to sleep and hypnosis and, therefore, requires a special method to achieve it.

To explain . . . if you are in hypnosis under the guidance

of an expert hypnotherapist, you cannot go directly from hypnosis to the normal sleep state, just with a command from the hypnotist. You will have seen stage hypnotists who say: 'When I snap my fingers, you will go to sleep,' or some similar instruction. The subject may *appear* to fall asleep, but it is *not* sleep in the sense of the word that we all understand when we are asleep in bed. Hypnosis is a state in which the subconscious *mimics* sleep. To use the stage analogy again, if you were genuinely asleep it would be pointless, because you would not be capable of hearing and following the hypnotist's instructions! To return briefly to a point I made in Chapter 1, perhaps now you will better understand why the use of the word 'sleep' in connection with hypnosis has caused so much confusion in the ordinary person's mind for so long.

To re-emphasise: *you have to come out of hypnosis to go to sleep!* As you are going to sleep at night, you go through a form of natural self-hypnosis – a daydream – before you sleep. But you come out of one state, that is, hypnosis, before you reach another, that is, sleep.

If you have listened to a hypnotic tape recording and you fell asleep during it, you will still have been through the same procedure. When a hypnotherapist has a client in hypnosis, the subject is always awake and even on the very rare occasions when they snore and look asleep, if you were to give them an instruction, for example to lift their hand or open their eyes, they will respond, proving they are not in a true form of sleep. So how does the hypnotherapist attain Hypno-Sleep? With good training in a specific method. Considering this is not yet taught in the UK, you could find it difficult to find a therapist who can do this for you.

So how can you do it yourself if an experienced therapist can't?

First, you can be sure that you will go to sleep every night, at one stage or another, therefore you know that you are able to have a period where you can practise very regularly – in fact, every night. There are certain words spoken when you are sleeping that will put you in this particular frame of mind and thus prepare you for accepting the suggestion at this ultra-deep level in sleep. Such a level of sleep is capable of accepting and following instructions.

You may have tried this when you were a kid as a childhood game, perhaps saying to your brother or sister while they were asleep that immediately they awoke their right foot would feel itchy – and sure enough, when they awoke they started to scratch their right foot!

But used as a therapy in sleep, the significant difference is that not only is the mind capable of accepting suggestions but it can also eliminate a trauma problem without bringing it forward to the conscious part of the mind to deal with. This marks a complete turnaround to conventional therapy.

With repetition of nine simple words, the inner mind can be switched on to co-operate: 'You can hear me – but you won't wake up.' Repeated a few times when you are asleep, these words allow the programming to proceed. It has been proved that your mind will not condition itself to self-destruct; therefore, in order to program you to harm yourself, a very thorough brainwashing technique would have to be used and this always includes special, mind-altering drugs. Therefore, there is no harm that can be done with conventional hypnosis, especially with your specially designed suggestion. If you have someone else to say the words while you are asleep, there could be a grey area of doubt here.

It may be possible, like in stage hypnotism, that your sleeping partner can program you to find them more desirable, likeable or trustworthy, etc. And if you wanted to do this anyway, then the unauthorised suggestion could be accepted. But why take the risk? Tape your own specially created suggestions or use the one provided, which has been prepared to begin after you are asleep.

One doctor who was also a well-known hypnotherapist used an adaptation of this type of method to help his marriage. He claimed that a few direct suggestions while his wife slept each night prevented the usual stream of arguments that normally occurred. He absolutely believed it saved his marriage.

Before I describe in detail the method, first a few pieces of advice to help you make it work . . . It is advisable not to take sleeping pills, as these may affect the success of the self-treatment.

This book comes with a ninety-minute tape. The first side contains an induction script designed to lead you into relaxation and hypnosis. It also includes a hypnotic suggestion for weight control.

Third – and most important – is a post-hypnotic suggestion, which is a form of instruction that directs your inner mind to accept the other side of the tape, which is the Hypno-Sleep technique. This side of the tape is designed to work only when you are *actually* asleep. This is the totally new concept which has not previously been thought possible.

The voice you will hear on the tape is my own. I also wrote the scripts that you will hear me reading. They are very carefully and specifically designed, each for a different and individual area of the mind. Side 1 is a traditional hypnotic suggestion aimed at the subconscious, which I like to think of as a sophisticated robot – an obedient servant which responds to commands. Side 2 is aimed at a part of the inner mind which operates at a much superior level, at the very core of your being.

You may find that the book and the tape are perfectly adequate and all you will need for the Hypno-Sleep method to work. However, there are other options. For instance, you may like to design your own tape with the instructions set out in Chapter 2 or choose from the scripts set out later in this chapter, which are designed to deal with specific situations. If you do choose to make your own tape, however, may I strongly recommend that you design your own scripts for *Side 1 only* and stick to the specially prepared Hypno-Sleep guide which is on Side 2.

When making your own tape, set the volume at a moderate level, not too loud but so that you can hear it comfortably without straining, rather like an audible whisper. Practise speaking your words on tape a few times and play them back before you make the actual recording, in order to ensure a smooth delivery. Recite your words clearly and precisely and at a gentle but confident pace – don't gabble or stutter, otherwise this could have a jarring effect on your relaxation and spoil the depth of the hypnosis.

Everything I have said above refers to Side 1 of your tape – the induction, the weight loss suggestion and the post-hypnotic suggestion which leads you into Side 2. You should listen to the whole of Side 1 *before* you go to bed – otherwise, if you feel sleepy and happen to fall asleep during it, then you will obviously not be able to turn the tape over to start playing the all-important Side 2.

Now we come to the Hypno-Sleep technique, where the *real* work will be done . . .

Put your tape on before you go to sleep and let it work while you are sleeping. If you find that the tape is disturbing your sleep, check whether the volume is too loud. If you continue to have problems, play Side 1 only for a few nights and then try again with the Hypno-Sleep method on Side 2 a little later. Experiment, say for a couple of weeks or so, with Side 1. Don't persevere with Side 2 if you are having problems sleeping, otherwise the frustration may disturb your sleep pattern.

If you are already having problems with insomnia, then you will have to solve this problem first, perhaps with suggestion hypnosis, before you can use the Hypno-Sleep method. If you find yourself lying awake through the Hypno-Sleep side of the tape because you have difficulty in sleeping anyway, then the worst that can happen is that the Hypno-Sleep suggestion will only work in the form of a more traditional hypnotic suggestion. This is harmless but not so effective, as the Hypno-Sleep is much more powerful.

When I had the treatment, I believed I was awake and could hear everything, rather like when you are having a dream that doesn't make sense. You hope it's a dream but you are not sure if it is reality. When you wake up, unless you write the contents down, you tend to remember only bits of it. When I had the Hypno-Sleep treatment – to get over the trauma of my father's death – I thought I was awake when the hypnotherapist, Jack Mason, was talking. But when I did eventually wake up, I could remember virtually nothing.

Because of this possible misinterpretation, do not despair if you think you are not asleep when the Hypno-Sleep tape is playing. You may well be asleep but in that dream-type reality state to which I referred. Judge the success or otherwise of the technique by whether it brings about a change in your behaviour. No change and it hasn't worked. If you sleep through the tape and start to see changes in your eating pattern, whether gradual or even spectacular, you know it is working. Everybody will react differently, some observing an immediate, dramatic change, while others may hardly notice – except they begin to lose weight without any effort and realise it later on.

This is a very new technique and harmless but, as with any DIY type of work, a modicum of common sense is needed. This book has been prepared so that if you are having trouble with the Hypno-Sleep technique you still can fall back on the conventional therapy of suggestion while in hypnosis.

One question you may, not unreasonably, be asking, is: how is my spouse or partner going to react to my playing a tape in the bedroom, with the likelihood of disturbing their own sleep?

You don't want to cause a potential rift in your relationship, especially if your partner is a light sleeper or suffers from insomnia, so you will have to compromise. Sleeping separately for a short time while you are practising the Hypno-Sleep may well help. Whatever you decide, make sure you are aware of your partner's sleeping comforts.

One possibility, of course, is to wear headphones. However, many people find these uncomfortable and impractical and a barrier to sleep. Ideally, it is better if you can have your tape recorder close by you, on the bedside table or chest, say, with the volume set at a reasonable level.

The specially devised scripts should not have any adverse affect on another person who may be sleeping with you. If they have a weight problem also, in fact, it should be beneficial to both of you. Even if they don't, then the worst it can do is coax them into a healthier life-style or eating regime, giving them more of an awareness of the effects of body abuse. Remember, the mind does not have a self-destruct program and will naturally edit out unwanted suggestions. Therefore, incorrect suggestions will not work. As I mentioned in an earlier chapter, even the most powerful stage hypnotist cannot make a person perform an act they do not want to do. But if you or your partner are in any way frightened of hypnosis, then don't undertake it.

Method for change

1 Read the book

Reading the book will give you an understanding of how the technique works and will help to encourage your belief system into accepting that you can change if you are willing to work at it.

2 Play Side 1 of the tape

As I have said, Side 1 is a specially prepared suggestion to encourage you to want to succeed in losing weight and to prepare you for the Hypno-Sleep. You must play this *before* going to sleep.

3 Just before you decide to go to sleep, start to play the second side of the tape. It works while you sleep.

This is the technique that sets new, desirable programs into motion, helping your inner mind to outlaw old and unwanted attitudes and reprogram them into a healthy lifestyle. Talking to the cells of the body via the inner mind demonstrates what is necessary to make changes. Because this is being done when you are asleep, you need the least amount of conscious effort to set this new attitude into play. The new attitude changes your behaviour and enthuses you to healthier eating and exercising your body more, which in turn ensures you are fitter, your body working as it should and your weight then reducing at a safe level.

The final chapter of this book, which includes suggestions for exercising and eating, is just a guideline for your interest.

If you are overweight, and a regular dieter who has tried lots of other slimming plans, you will probably already possess an encyclopaedic knowledge for weight loss. Once you have read the book and used the Hypno-Sleep tape, your inner mind will use these resources in a more responsible way for you to eat properly – for you. It will create a natural, specially prepared diet that you don't need to think about. You just desire healthy food and can't understand why anyone, including yourself, would want to eat otherwise. This does not stop you from indulging in a treat now and again – but it is as a slim person would occasionally have a sweet or chocolate. In other words, no big deal.

But, again, remember – everybody is different. What works for someone else may be incorrect for your digestion, so go with your instincts. Just regard the final chapter as a means of generating information for your inner mind to work with.

ALL ABOUT SUGGESTION HYPNOSIS

'The subconscious has to obey suggestions as though they were orders. The knack is to get the orders through to the subconscious. Not always possible via the conscious.'

Self-hypnosis as a therapy

In this section, I will be telling you how you can construct your own suggestions for use in self-hypnosis. The construction for a suggestion is extremely important, so much so that if you don't get the composition right the hypnosis may not be successful. There are certain rules that are applicable when compiling your suggestion but these are by no means hard and fast. For example, the stop smoking suggestion I have been using for years is full of negative words – generally considered a 'no no' in many hypnosis circles – but it has been extremely successful.

When dealing with the mind there are many variables and so what works for one may not work for another. However, the rules listed below are a good safeguard when designing your own individual script. It is much more effective to stick to one problem at a time, so as not to overload the work to be done by the subconscious.

Remember also that one person may feel happier with flowery words describing in detail the wonders of the scenery, while someone else may find this uninteresting. Therefore, I have included two different approaches to suggestions in the examples in the next few pages.

The rules I have chosen are important for formulating a powerful suggestion. If you have applied them and you are still not getting a result, then you should consider seeking the services of an advanced hypnotherapist.

Developing your own plan

How to hypnotise yourself

The three options for self-hypnosis are covered in Chapter 2, but briefly, if you choose to do so without a helper, then read through the rules below. You can either personalise your own script or use the ones provided. When you have chosen your script, then put it on a cassette tape. Practise it until you are satisfied that your voice is soothing and even. Begin by leaving a couple of seconds of silence; this is to allow you time to get from the tape machine to wherever you are going to relax and to have time to compose yourself. Make sure you are comfortable, either sitting or lying, legs uncrossed, hands by your sides and neck supported. Your tape should begin with the progressive relaxation and be followed by the appropriate suggestion, then the script for the count out of hypnosis. You can use the first or third person on the tape – for example, either 'You feel more confident,' or 'I feel more confident . . . '

When you are reading the progressive induction, use a slow, monotone type of voice, while the actual suggestion should be more enthusiastic and businesslike. The count out of hypnosis, on the other hand, should be done in a strong and forceful voice still holding the enthusiasm.

How to hypnotise yourself without the aid of a tape recorder

Not everyone has the equipment for taping themselves for the induction and a few people may suffer from technophobia, or a fear of technology. So, for the person who doesn't want to, or can't, use a tape recorder, then you need to memorise the progressive script (or buy a tape recording of a hypnotic relaxation). Use this method for the induction: before you start with the hypnosis, prepare your script and read it aloud a couple of times. Pick a word that signifies what change you want; for example, if you wanted to sleep more soundly, you could choose 'slumber'. This is the trigger word you will be using to program your subconscious.

When you have relaxed yourself, either by a tape recording or just mentally going through the progressive relaxation in your mind's eye, then, at the point you have finished your induction, just instruct your subconscious to come forward in the form of a picture or thought and whatever comes forward in your mind's eye – even if it's a blank – say your key word, 'slumber'.

This will pre-program your subconscious for change. Your mind will have accepted the suggestion in your short-term memory when you took the time to study and read it aloud, as instructed beforehand. The word, 'slumber' (in this case), just acts as a trigger word. It is like pressing the enter key on a computer which begins the program. Therefore, your mind should now have accepted the new information. The two major obstacles to prevent the work going ahead would be either if you hadn't attained hypnosis or if the problem was linked with an earlier trauma. Then, such a trauma would have to be dealt with before the new program could go ahead, although repetition of the above may in time eliminate the hold which the trauma has.

There are hundreds of different and varied methods to activate self-hypnosis but, unfortunately, not everyone finds it satisfactory. I still recommend having a helper to attain the hypnosis for the very first time, then you can use short cuts and hypnotise yourself.

Twelve rules for formulating a suggestion

You don't have to be a genius at the English language to be able to write your own suggestions. But these are some guidelines you should follow which will aid you in making your suggestions clear, positive and, thus, more likely to result in success.

- Use the Present Tense
- Be Positive
- Be Specific
- Be Detailed
- Be Simple
- Use Exciting and Imaginative Words
- Affirm Activity
- Be Accurate
- Be Realistic
- Personalise
- Symbolise Your Suggestion
- Be Repetitive

Use the present tense

1 Always suggest that you are already acting out the behaviour change, for example, 'I am' or 'I have'.

2 The only exception to the rule is a physical condition, for example, a broken leg. Then use a progressive form of the present tense, such as 'My leg heals quickly and comfortably.' You can add, 'My leg heals in half the time it would normally take,' to lock in a time element.

3 Direct suggestions for future behaviour must also be

in the present tense, for example, 'I always feel comfortable in company . . . ', 'day by day, I feel more enthusiastic about . . . ' or 'I am more confident'.

Be positive

1 Eliminate negative words and phrases, for example, 'I am not', 'I don't'.

2 Don't mention what you are trying to change. Create the mental picture of what you want to move towards as if it has already happened, for example say, 'I am more confident,' *NOT* 'I will be more confident.' Or say, 'I never feel self-conscious,' *NOT* 'I would like to feel self-confident.'

Be specific

1 Confine your suggestions to one area, *NOT* to a collection of problems, for example say, 'I feel confident,' or 'I control my weight,' or 'I sleep fitfully,' but not all three in the same sentence!

2 It's like the lazy man's load, where he carries far too much so that he won't have to make a return journey, resulting in him dropping everything he is carrying and making more work for himself in the end. Don't overload your subconscious with a selection of major problems.

Be detailed

1 Analyse your goal and structure your suggestion to cover every detail of your changed behaviour attitude.

2 Don't just say you want to succeed, detail how and what goals you would like to reach. For example, how

much money you wish to earn or what size of business you require for you to attain your goal in life. Otherwise, the subconscious being so literal, it may just believe that keeping a roof over your head and food in the larder is successful, because you've neglected to explain how successful you want to be.

Don't forget, your ideas of success are changing constantly as you mature and progress. You don't want your subconscious to act on out-of-date information; therefore, you reprogram by imagination and visualisation. Just imagine if your idea of success as a child was simply getting a job. That's all your subconscious would be programmed for if you just said you wanted to be successful. Consciously, you may want riches but subconsciously you already have success if you have a job (which means any job), so it believes the instructions have already been carried out and so no further work is done. Have you ever wondered why some people stay in the same job they loathe, year after year, all of their working life?

Be simple

1 Speak to your subconscious as if you are talking to a toddler. Keep the words simple. The subconscious may well be very sophisticated but there is less chance of confusion if you keep the wording plain. The English language is full of words that have innuendoes and double meanings, so think carefully before you give your orders to your subconscious.

I knew an American hypnotherapist who for years wanted to give up smoking. She also was consistently worried about her weight. In hypnosis, she instructed her subconscious to replace the satisfaction for smoking by becoming thin. The word 'thin' was the problem. Thin in her conscious mind meant slim, but subconsciously it took the word literally. She became painfully thin, just as she had instructed. She looked dreadful but, like the anorexic, she thought she looked slim. Also, this self-inflicted program had included an extensive fitness regime to make sure no weight was put on. It was more a fitness obsession, having to keep running a few miles a day to ensure she kept 'thin'. She would keep up the regime of running, however impractical it was – even to the extent to having to go out running in the tea break of a convention when everyone else was enjoying socialising. This was a perfect example of a communication breakdown between the conscious and the subconscious.

Use exciting and imaginative words

1 The subconscious reacts to emotive words.
2 Make your suggestions full of feeling and excitement. Strong words have impact, probably because they may have been used in fairy stories or comic books and, even though buried deep in the subconscious files, when located are still power words and therefore have impact.

Use powerful words (energy words), such as *exciting, wonderful, dynamic*.

These words may sound clumsy but to the subconscious they will be acted on as the true meaning, and encourage a change. Although the words may seem uncomfortable to the acting home therapist, words you may not generally use, to the person in hypnosis they are very soothing, comfortable and encourage enthusiasm.

Affirm Activity

1 Suggest the *exact* improvement you wish to achieve.

2 It is of little benefit to say: 'I would like to be . . .' or 'I will feel better'. The subconscious doesn't respond to ability as much as action. The word 'will' suggests a future action and could be misconstrued by the subconscious as in the 'distant' future, for example, '(*Sometime in the future*) I will feel better.' This request has been diluted with the possibility of the silent instruction. It gives the subconscious an 'out' because it could be requesting a change ten years hence; there has not been a time limit locked into the suggestion. It may help you to understand the importance if you can imagine a mother asking her little boy to tidy his room or get changed. She may repeat the instruction a few times without any response. It is only when she says 'Now', with determination, that the child seriously takes notice. The word 'now' locks in the time structure. 'I am relaxed/confident' etc, has more chance of being accepted as a new program with immediate action.

Be accurate

1 Plan out the details of the improvement. 'I feel healthy' is not specific enough. If you have an illness or even something as simple as a cold, say what you want, within reason that is. 'I am recovering rapidly. With each new day I feel better and better,' would be more appropriate.

Be realistic

There are circumstances where it is wrong to suggest perfection, for example 'I am happy all the time'. This would obviously *not* be realistic, say at a funeral.

Personalise

1 Structure suggestions for the change in yourself, your attitudes and actions.

2 As you change, others associated with you change. The easiest way to activate change in the people around you is to change yourself. For example, if you have a relationship that is suffering from constant arguments and you stop responding to negativity from your partner, they will have to change and either find a new way of aggravating you or this act in itself may stop the arguments. Whatever the outcome, there will be a change in your partner's strategy.

Therefore, you can pre-program yourself to react totally indifferently to a word or phrase that normally would stimulate your anger. For example, 'Each time my partner/friend/someone says [offending words] I feel relaxed and calm, knowing that I am now in control of my emotions . . . my subconscious deals with any negative emotions, constructively channelling them to my advantage . . . allowing me to be relaxed and calm.'

It may be appropriate to have an anger release suggestion prior to this suggestion. If you have a locked-in anger about a person or circumstance, it can cause deep anxiety and rage and even affect your health. A good anger suggestion can dissipate the unwanted reactions.

Symbolise your suggestion

1 Picture yourself as you want to be. In your imagination, build a detailed picture. Don't worry if it's exaggerated as long as there is a modicum of possibility. That gives you a gigantic scope, as most dreams are possible if you are willing to work at them.

When I lived in California in the early 1980s I was told that the government would never clamp down on drink driving, as the liquor barons had too much money involved in politics. While we in the UK had the breathalyser, if you were stopped by the police in the States for drinking and driving they would use old and outmoded tests to see if you were over the limit. You had to walk a straight line or bring your forefinger to your nose without faltering.

Many innocent people were getting mowed down by drunken drivers. It was even a good method of committing murder by pretending to be drunk and running your victim over, with sometimes only a fine as punishment.

One mother had not one but *two* children killed by drunken drivers. She decided to campaign, so she channelled all her anger and disgust into getting justice and stop it happening to others. She put her full energy into changing the law, concentrating every moment on making her feelings public. She was just an ordinary housewife but now, with total single-mindedness, she persevered against all odds and within only months she was joined by other mothers. They picketed, found a good slogan that attracted television coverage – 'MADD' (Mothers Against Drunk Drivers) – and changed history in only a short time. Now, the laws in the States are stricter than ours. Virtually nothing is impossible.

Be repetitive

Use repetition but in variable words and convincing adjectives, so your suggestion is attractive. It's a little like selling a product. The more often you picture an idea, the more of a possibility it becomes. For an example, when you see old styles that look so bizarre and outdated, like the mini skirt, platform heels, bell bottoms and so on, only a few years ago they looked appallingly out of date. But when you are exposed to those same styles by the media and constantly told that this is now the latest in fashion trends, you start to become accustomed to this old/new look and the more you see it the less outlandish it seems.

With the above guides to suggestions, you can either use one of the structured suggestions included as a base or change it to suit your individual needs. You may decide even to design the whole suggestion yourself. If you want to design one for someone else, you need to find out exactly what changes they are expecting and work the information around one of the basic scripts.

If it concerns a sport, say, and it hasn't been covered in the book, you need the information of what skills the individual is expected to develop in order to play well. You can find this information out from an expert in that particular sport and then include this information in the script. For example, to play tennis, one of the problems for beginners is that they tend to move their eyes automatically away from the ball just before they hit it with the racket and often miss or don't hit it straight. This is a habit that needs to be created.

If you put the instruction in the suggestion while you, or the subject who wants to learn, is in hypnosis, then you will have created a new habit without the practice that is usually needed without hypnosis. An example of this instruction would be: 'Your eyes stay fixed on the ball until your racket strikes it, which enables you to direct the ball exactly where you want it to go. Your co-ordination is perfect, your arm movements are strong and positive when leading your racket to hit the ball to its destination. You are fully confident in your co-ordination.'

As a general rule, it has been accepted that the scripts for suggestions have to be long and repetitive. By accident, I found this wasn't necessarily so. When I developed the speed-reading technique I found that a short, direct instruction was all that was necessary. Which is all well and good for experienced therapists who have the skill and, having already gained the subject's confidence, can prove their ability by demonstrating a profound, deep hypnosis. But for the amateur, without the confidence of experience, the long descriptive script generates confidence in the hypnosis from the client.

The suggestion is introduced when the subject is already in hypnosis but first I'd like to reassure the subject that they can reject any suggestions that are inappropriate. This alleviates worries the subject may still be harbouring about being brainwashed. So, I like to prepare the subconscious with the following short, comforting words *after* the progressive relaxation but *preceding* the suggestion.

A *quality-of-life-plan to a better future*

When you have succeeded in hypnotising yourself, a quick daily input of three impact words, that literally takes seconds, will start to make permanent your desired changes – without the need for lengthy suggestions.

First of all, find three powerful words that epitomise the changes you want to make – powerful words like Successful, Dynamic, Charismatic, Fully Confident, etc. Choose three words that you feel realise your wishes. When you have quickly put yourself in self-hypnosis, access your subconscious by instructing it to come forward in the form of a picture or a thought. You can use the same picture or thought each time, if you feel comfortable, or wait for one to come at random. Then say the three words privately in your mind and, as you say them, picture yourself on a TV screen behaving this way. Then just open your eyes.

Do this every day for at least three weeks and you will start to see changes in your attitudes. It is a simple blueprint for improvement. The rehearsal in your mind is important to show your subconscious just what you want. When you practise self-hypnosis you will soon be able just to close your eyes and be immediately in hypnosis, so this method is very quick and powerful.

How to design your own weight loss tape

The hypnotic suggestion is a script that follows the relaxation induction, which you were given in Chapter 2. I like to include what I call a pre-suggestion which prepares your inner mind for your main suggestion. The words are a form of security and, indeed, a further instruction to allow the mind to edit out unwanted or unnecessary data.

Pre-suggestion

'In this deep and special sleep . . . your inner mind . . . for your protection . . . is aware what is happening around you . . . so the chosen suggestions, for your benefit, go directly to your subconscious mind . . . there, they are accepted because these ideas are for your benefit. These thoughts become firmly fixed in your inner mind . . . embedded . . . so they remain with you, long after you wake up . . . helping you want to change those things you want to change for your own sake.'

This pre-suggestion is then followed by the weight suggestion of your choice. Suggestions are a selection of words that are specially arranged to include instructions and are carefully compiled with the intention of encouraging a change of attitude that in turn brings about a change in behaviour pattern. So, just read through the following suggestions and choose the one that suits you best.

Suggestion for weight control

This is the full transcript of Side 1 on your suggestion

hypnosis tape. You can use the one provided or prepare your own scripts from the information in this chapter. Your inner mind or subconscious, as it is referred to, will be shortened to just 'mind' in the suggestion for your convenience.

'*Your inner mind is now being re-trained for a new and beneficial programme . . . one of healthy living . . . both in eating and looking after your body . . . your mind is programmed for harmony . . . your mind instructs your body cells to work towards health and being fit . . . eating healthy . . . keeping fit . . . ensuring optimum health . . . and releasing and solving trauma related problems . . . that have been obstructing you from being healthy . . . from now on you feel . . . look . . . and act . . . healthy.*

'*Your body responds to your healthy eating and works efficiently . . . your mind now instructs you to eat healthy and desirable foods . . . your mind allows you to enjoy healthy eating . . . every bit as much as you . . . used to . . . enjoy unhealthy food . . . you see unhealthy food for what it is . . . a chemical mishmash that is only harmful to your body . . . you realise how many spoonfuls of sugar are condensed in sweets and chocolates . . . the false food taste other fatty products have . . . to make them desirable. You are now more aware of the dangers of these additives and unnatural substances to your whole being . . . and especially to your longevity.*

'*No more . . . no more . . . it is time to stop using your body as a rubbish bin . . . you treat your body as an immaculate, wonderful carriage . . . for your mind . . . and you treat it accordingly . . . as you relax even more, you imagine yourself eating healthily and enjoying your new lifestyle . . . you see yourself projected on a mirror in your mind's eye and you see your reflection as it is now . . . now, allow your reflection gradually to slim . . . notice how happy you look as you see the weight reducing . . . now, add another mirror at the side of the original one . . . on this new mirror project your image exactly how slim you want to be . . . make sure this is a realistic shape . . . realistic to your own type of build . . . now check with the other mirror and see the difference . . . you are programming your mind for success . . . your subconscious mind needs to be shown precisely what you want to attain . . . and, therefore, each night you work on your mirror image . . . for a few moments just before you sleep and as you awake . . . always using your two mirrors, one to work on showing the gradual reductions . . . and the second to show your ultimate goal. This simple mind work will direct your subconscious and . . . eventually . . . become a habit . . . a new program, programmed to succeed.*

'Whenever you use your Hypno-Sleep suggestion while you are sleeping, your inner mind allows you to sleep while the important changes are carried out . . . changes in attitude to begin to bring back that natural self-discipline and common sense which helps you to eat correctly, healthily and enjoyably. The slim person does this naturally . . . if they eat too much or treat themselves occasionally, then they adjust their eating to compensate for the extra food . . . and soon you will, too.'

Side 2 – the suggestion for hypno-sleep
The following is an example of the suggestion that is used in the new, revolutionary self-help therapy of Hypno-Sleep. This suggestion is carefully prepared for anyone with an extra weight problem and is all that you need to instruct your inner mind to repair possibly buried traumas and prepare for new, desirable eating habits. The first few words are very important and need to be repeated. While asleep, this short instruction puts your sleeping mind into a receptive mode.

'You can hear me . . . but you won't wake up . . . you can hear me . . . but you won't wake up . . . you can hear me . . . but you won't wake up . . . you can hear me . . . but you won't wake up.

'You have been over-eating now for . . . t-o-o l-o-n-g . . . the results are your body is becoming unsightly and fat . . . it is bad for your self-esteem . . . and, more important, it is very bad for your health. This over-eating is making your body overwork . . . stretching your resources, your energy that would normally be used to help you progress . . . preventing you from attaining your goals in life.

'Your goals may be simple . . . just to be happy . . . or more complex . . . to be rich and famous . . . whatever your dreams may be . . . you are sabotaging them. Instead of using your valuable energy needed to progress, to go forward . . . you are using it in a negative way . . . to think repetitive and unnecessary thoughts . . . constant thoughts of food . . . eating . . . and all the strategy that goes with the plans to over-eat . . . wasted time . . . all this effort and time used . . . when eating is just for living and should be

only a small part of your everyday pattern.

'In the past there may have been a very good reason for you to over-eat . . . a very good reason for you to derive comfort, protection or even punishment from over-eating . . . but from now on your inner mind can sort these problems out . . . put them to rest. This wonderful work happens while you are sleeping . . . your deep inner mind is there to protect you and from experience allows you to eat correctly . . . correctly for you. You have all the knowledge at your disposal to begin a new program . . . a program of health.

'Now you see food that is good for you . . . you see healthy food as good . . . and as exciting as any of the unhealthy food you used to like. Your passion for . . . chocolates or sweets or unhealthy, fatty foods . . . now substituted with healthy foods.

'Being healthy and fit gives you a wonderful feeling of accomplishment . . . achievement . . . knowing your mind is working with your body now . . . in harmony . . . over-riding the need for negative, unhealthy eating with wonderful nutritious foods . . . eating less, eating substantial healthy foods, until your body reaches your desired and healthy weight . . . your body regulates your food intake . . . until you reach your credible goals . . . so you lose weight while being perfectly safe for your body to cope and retrain.

'Your deep inner mind alters the incorrect . . . out-of-date . . . program of overeating . . . to eating properly . . . that is to nourish you and energise you for optimum efficiency . . . a streamlined and healthy you.

'As you eat less, your metabolism is very effective and you feel full of energy . . . you find you can exercise your body and limbs . . . so they too can benefit . . . and work efficiently . . . you feel wonderful . . . and proud of your success . . . success at ridding yourself of unnecessary traumas . . . related to your over-eating . . . traumas that were responsible for your overweight . . . you don't have to think about it . . . your deep inner mind works this all out while you sleep, orchestrating your body and cells to work efficiently for your new healthy life . . . all you know is you enjoy eating healthier . . . and you find it easier to exercise your body but in such a way it is a pleasure. When you are at your desired but realistic weight your mind instructs your body to keep you at this optimum level . . . and you are now free . . . free to enjoy your life.'

I have included two different styles of suggestions to suit different types of people. You can either use them as they are or design your own from the instructions laid out in this chapter.

Type 1. is for general use.

Type 2. There has definitely been a move to alternatives recently – alternative food, medicine, and thinking. Many people are more aware, looking to be healthier in both mind and body, and have adopted a kind of esoteric attitude. This suggestion is selected with this type of person in mind.

General introduction

The general introduction is used after the pre-suggestion and just before your chosen suggestion. You can edit this to your specific requirements. Some people like long suggestions in hypnosis, while others prefer short ones. These suggestions are prepared to give you options. Perhaps you prefer to use the full suggestion first, then cut it short for a repetitive, daily hypnosis. I would suggest you listen to the tape provided, or your own tape, at least once a day for a minimum of three weeks. In extensive research, it has been calculated that it generally takes approximately three weeks to develop a habit. When you read the rules of suggestion in this chapter, it is explained that the subconscious takes words literally and so what may sound old-fashioned and elaborate to you now has a much better impact in hypnosis than you realise.

'Now is as good as any time to put your own life into perspective . . . a time to be honest with yourself . . . to see clearly where your life is going. Many people have their opinions about size, shape and weight . . . let them . . . that's their problem, not yours . . . all you have to do in life is to find a way of living that truly makes you happy . . . not just happy to be sociable but really content . . . living joyously with no "if only's".

'Put simply . . . living life to the full, feeling the thrill of being alive and busting with vitality! It's easy to take on the habit of "acting happy". If you could swap your life with anyone in the world, would you choose to swap? If you answered yes, then you are not completely happy inside your skin . . . now is as good a time as any to change your life . . . not just a little bit . . . not to make some changes here and there but to change your life completely.

'The real you will start living from today . . . as you

relax even more you begin to feel an inner peace as you image yourself improving . . . now, look deep inside yourself, that is where your life force lives . . . a bright shining light . . . your light is as bright as the brightest star . . . nobody's light is brighter than yours. Everybody is equally gifted with this light . . . this is the truth . . . we are all stars.

'What is also true is that many people have forgotten this . . . it may be due to things that have happened to them or said to them . . . perhaps they just had unrealistic expectations of other people! Sometimes, stories told to us as children lead us, as adults, to believe that life has not been fair to us . . . for whatever reason that people have forgotten . . . they find it harder to see their own light . . . they see it as somehow a bit duller than others . . . these reasons that get in the way are not real . . . they are simply our version of an experience long gone . . . no more real than yesterday's cloud.

'Clouds are like hurts . . . they are continuously changing but they can also disappear completely without trace . . . gone for ever . . . once the clouds are gone, the rapture you can experience, just by witnessing your own light, defies description. But one thing is for sure . . . you'll want to sing, and dance, to express yourself and take part in life's rich tapestry, you will be the weaver not the watcher . . . you won't be bothered by anything that anybody thinks about you . . . you will be free.

'Never again will you involve yourself in activities that dull your senses . . . only the best is good enough for you . . . with your new level of awareness, you recognise *that simplest really is best and that it really is true, that "the best things in life are free". Even more curious, as you "free", you became one of "the best things in life" ... you begin to realise your full potential ... charismatic, magnetic, inspirational, funny, spontaneous, sexy and wise ... free from your past, free of guilt, free of fear and free to savour every moment of your amazing life.*

'*Never again will someone or something change the way you eat ... never again will you internalise your problems. You will deal with them on the outside of your body. We all encounter ups and downs ... that is life! ... but it doesn't have to affect the way you live. Just remember ... into each life a little rain must fall, but as you learn to provide the sunshine, you will find yourself covered in rainbows.*'

Choose one of the following suggestions which is most suitable for you and then you can either add to the above or use directly after the pre-suggestion. Otherwise, you can design your own from the rules of suggestion earlier in this chapter and utilise from the following examples:

For those seriously overweight
'*Nothing about your looks can make you a good person or a bad person ... being big is not bad but it's unhealthy ... it's unhealthy for the body and can lead to an unhealthy outlook on life ... some people think that fat people are happy people ... they may be but they are also experts in covering up.*

'*People who are currently overweight have a habit of eating just a bit too much ... over a period of time it builds up and as they get heavier they exercise less, making it even* worse . . . they are very aware of the physical restrictions that this puts on their ability to live life to the full . . . healthy people look healthy, breathe easily, and lead balanced lives . . . only eating what they need . . . they enjoy being energetic . . . running and being agile . . . and have no problem finding really nice clothes to wear . . . healthy people tend not to sweat much and don't generally have problems with their joints . . . their social life is as active as they want it to be . . . they can go anywhere and believe the best time to do something is now.

'This is how your life will become as you eat less and get fitter . . . no longer will you feel the need to cover up your light by covering yourself with fat . . . no longer will you punish yourself with the extra burden of holding on to pointless guilt . . . you won't be needy of love or attention, so you won't eat to make yourself feel better . . . no longer will you need to cover yourself with fat to protect yourself . . . the fat would make you look less attractive but now you do not fear the attention because you will only attract nice people.

'There's also no way that you'd try to look more cherubic or want to reclaim the innocence of being a baby, because you know that your light cannot be tainted by an experience . . . your light is as pure and as bright now as it ever was . . . you will simply start eating less and at regular meal times only . . . eating late and snacking are things of the past . . . you find that sweet things are just too sickly for your more refined palate . . . you never realised just how good fresh fruit and vegetables taste and you start to enjoy drinking water . . . your weight loss will be gradual and safe *and as you shed the bulk, you'll find exercise more and more appealing . . . before long, you won't recognise the old you but everyone will want to know the new you.'*

For those slightly overweight
'Because you now wish to live your life to the full, you want to get rid of that extra bit of weight that you are carrying around with you . . . you've recognised that waiting around on the edges of life is just not good enough . . . no compromises . . . you are now ready to move into the fast lane . . . to take your rightful place among the happy people who enjoy the freedom of life without the worry of extra weight.

'Inside, you know that you're no different from them . . . it's just that you don't feel quite as vital or as healthy as them. To claim your energy, you start to eat smaller, healthier portions of quality, healthy food . . . your subconscious inner mind brings back that natural discipline of healthy eating . . . food takes energy to digest and the richer the food, the more energy it takes to break it down . . . having more energy in your system will raise your metabolic rate, making your digestion even more efficient . . . combined with regular exercise the results are stunning . . . steadily, but safely, the weight comes off and the toned body emerges . . . which makes you feel great.

'This, in turn, allows you to appreciate what you've got and how attractive, both in mind and body, you are to others . . . learning to look after yourself is where you learn to love yourself . . . when you hear people talking about the happy people you know they are also talking about you.'

For those with bulimia

Bulimia is a little bit like when a dog chases its tail and never actually gets anywhere. Having gorged themselves, the bulimic binger then throws up. People with such a disorder can eat gigantic amounts of food before they force their fingers down their throat to induce themselves to be sick. Usually, the bulimic will binge on unhealthy foods and fatty foods and not always food that they enjoy.

I had a girl who came to my rooms with bulimia. I asked her what was the last thing she ate before she saw me. 'Six pieces of bread,' she announced. And then she added proudly: 'But I didn't eat any butter on them.' It was pretty obvious to me that she wasn't eating for pleasure – a sure sign of a trauma-related eating disorder. It turned out that she had wanted to stay a 'Daddy's little girl', so her subconscious had arranged it by keeping her body podgy. The program had never been erased when she became an adult. When she had finished the treatment, she was able to eat and enjoy her food. This was a brand-new experience for her. She had been eating for so long to be podgy and her throwing up was to keep her figure in the correct proportions.

Bulimics sometimes share similarities with each other. They are often perfectionists and expect a lot from themselves, although inside they tend to have a low self-esteem. However, they can be quite health-conscious when they are not bingeing. The bingeing begins as a comfort and escalates to a sense of shame and disgust. Like anorexia, it can be dangerous, as bulimics tends to have a relatively high suicide rate.

The bulimic causes terrible damage inside the body – to the gums, teeth, the stomach, the kidneys and by dehydration; these are only a few of the problems that can be caused by constant vomiting.

Suggestion for bulimia
'You have taken a great step in your life . . . by choosing not to be bulimic you are choosing not to beat yourself up. The body's ability to vomit is rarely called upon naturally . . . it was never designed to vomit on a daily basis . . . it causes damage to the stomach, as well as rotting your teeth . . . you used to experience the need to eat in binges but, before digesting, up you'd make it come, vital stomach acids and all . . . we would never force this behaviour upon someone else and now you've decided to stop doing it to yourself.

'The reasons that you are now able to stop are because you are now enjoying the taste of what you are eating . . . not just pushing food down . . . in order to binge . . . and because you are eating sensible amounts . . . there's no need to vomit any more.'

For those with anorexia
This is a very frightening eating disease and, unfortunately, the victim either does not realise it or will not accept they have the problem at all. I have treated clients who have had this problem but usually they have been brought to me by one of their relatives – they do not believe they have a problem themselves. I can only hope that if the person is constantly being told they may have anorexia, this may

invite them to consider the possibility and entice them to read further.

Anorexia is one of the few psychological disorders that is so serious that it can lead directly to death. Because the anorexic rarely seeks help, they usually end up having to be hospitalised when their condition is so critical that they collapse. They also resent any treatment and will deceive and lie to carry on the not-eating programme. Although research has not really shown what type of person will get anorexia, there has been a common denominator of poor self-image.

I have included a lengthy narration in the actual suggestion because, if it was written beforehand, the anorexic would probably skim over this information and ignore it, casually editing it out of the conscious mind, which in turn is part of their problem. The advantage of hypnosis is that this information which the conscious does not want is not edited out and is, therefore, allowed to seep through to the inner mind where it can be used to change attitudes that eventually change behaviour. Remember that the inner mind has the function to edit harmful suggestions, so there is no fear of dangerous information being planted there.

Being aware is one of the most effective weapons in fighting anorexia. You may have been developing anorexia for reasons other than dieting – the break-up of a love affair or some other such trauma that stops you wanting to eat for such a long period that it becomes a habit.

My mother suffered anorexia when she went through a series of what were thought to be at the time neurotic disorders. Years went by, when it was later found that she had a growth inside the back of her head which caused her to have physical discomfort when she ate. She simply stopped eating properly, hiding her food and pretending everything was OK. This was in the early seventies, when little was known about such a problem.

In the early eighties, I suffered a break-up of a love affair and, because I had been aware of my mother's illness, I recognised the symptoms and realised I was becoming anorexic. I fought it by asking my friends to force me to eat. I will never forget the taste of the food as I tried to put it into my mouth!

The strange thing was that I would be hungry, start to eat, and as soon as I attempted to put the food in my mouth, the hunger changed to distaste. This gave me an extra problem of trying to get rid of the food without looking ridiculous. I hadn't noticed the condition until it was too late. I just ate less and lost weight. At first I thought it was wonderful, being so slim. Then when I began to realise I had a sort of anorexia, I forced myself out of it only because I was aware of the potential outcome. I lost my bust and it took two years to recover my shape. I still remember people saying to me: 'I wish I had anorexia, so that I could lose weight.' They had no idea how ridiculous and even cruel this remark was to me and how annoyed it made me feel at the time.

But I won the battle and have never had any repercussions since. Fortunately, I did not have a self-image problem and had developed anorexia from just not eating.

Suggestion for anorexia

'Like you, everybody likes to look good . . . but anorexia nervosa is an addictive behaviour pattern . . . it occurs when people stop eating properly . . . and then goes on to trigger one of the human body's amazing survival responses. Unfortunately, the victims of this eating disorder don't realise they have it . . . but the signs are certainly there . . . other people mention that you are looking thin or casually hint that you should be careful not to lose any more weight . . . if you have had remarks like this, then you should really start to look at yourself.

'If your food has no taste . . . or tastes like sawdust when you put it into your mouth . . . and you have to try and dispose of it without being seen . . . beware, you may have anorexia. Like the alcoholic, unless you know you have a problem you cannot deal with it . . . looking in the mirror is not enough . . . the mind is fooled into thinking you need to lose more weight . . . that is part of the problem . . . so while you are in this wonderful, relaxed state, you can imagine the truth. Imagine a mirror in your mind's eye . . . the mirror of truth . . . project on to that mirror your own image . . . your own image without your clothes . . . look at your body . . . does it look healthy or thin? . . . are your arms too slim? . . . look at your bottom . . . is it as it should be? . . . look at yourself as if you were seeing yourself for the first time . . . and give an opinion on how you look.

'This image is for you to work on . . . to begin to get into better shape and move the word and the image from thin to slim . . . now let that image fade away while you relax even more . . . while you are so relaxed, just allow your inner *mind to take in some information to help you deal with your weight problem.*

'Crash dieting is the most common cause of the first stage of anorexia . . . poor nourishment of the brain affects the brain's ability to perceive your shape and weight properly . . . this can lead to a painfully thin person thinking that they still need to lose weight . . . not thinking straight can lead to other problems, both emotional and also in the workplace.

'Women often stop having periods, which can set off even more emotional problems . . . then, the second stage, the real problem, is when the body becomes so run-down that it goes into survival mode . . . it reacts as if you were stuck in the desert and unable to find food . . . rather than let you fall asleep to die, it releases substances in the brain called endorphins . . . to give you a chemical high . . . In the desert this "rush" could be exactly what you need to save your life . . . your mind alive but your body in a type of hibernation . . . your metabolism slowed down, so your need to eat is minimal and you lose weight very slowly . . . but because you have no extra weight to lose, you lose from your major storage areas . . . your arms, your breasts and your bottom . . . when these major stores are depleted, then you are dying . . . your body is eating itself in its fight to live.

'In the Western world, where so many people are obsessed by the way they look, rather than their happiness . . . this euphoric state can become a dangerous trap . . . for when an anorexic person starts to eat, the body stops releasing the endorphins and the euphoric

state disappears . . . *eating is clearly the healthy option but the addiction to the body's survival drug confuses the issue . . . if the brain were not being poorly nourished in the first place, the choice between eating and dying would be straightforward.*

'*The brain is more advanced than any computer on earth but it needs to be fed properly, just as a computer needs a regular supply of electricity . . . starving the brain is like pulling out some of the connections for a while . . . a properly balanced diet, taking in all the vitamin requirements, will lead to a healthy mind and a healthy body . . . too thin is as dangerous as too fat . . . crash dieting can damage the heart and kidneys . . . so don't even think about it . . . it is no longer an option to you . . . eating sensibly at regular meal times, combined with exercise, will its own does not work.*'

The three main trauma-related reasons for over-eating are comfort, protection and punishment. Usually, this information is brought out in advanced hypnotherapy. But if you already have an idea which one you may be suffering from, I have selected suggestions for all three. If you have chosen incorrectly, such a suggestion will not be damaging because your inner mind will make the selections which are appropriate, if any, for you.

It is OK to be fat
'*Enough is enough . . . you've tried burying your head in the sand . . . it hasn't worked . . . you are not happy as you are . . . who said "It's OK to be fat?" . . . you did . . . fat people are not bad people, but they do lead restricted lives*

. . . *it's because you have now chosen to live your life without restriction and live it to the full that you now recognise that being fat really doesn't suit you . . . that's the hardest part done . . . once you recognised that it may be OK for other people to be fat but that it's no longer what you want, the changes start to take place . . . immediately.*

'The moment you recognise that you want to live a full life as a healthy person . . . your life changes . . . you broaden your horizons and enhance the quality of your life . . . second best, no more . . . you can wear nice clothes . . . enjoy a better lifestyle . . . have self-confidence . . . and no limits . . . that's what's in store for you.

'A suitable change emerges . . . you are happy to trade rich food . . . for a richer life . . . making a decision and sticking to it not only enhances your life, it also raises your self-esteem . . . you'll be amazed just how many things in your life will change so effortlessly . . . the thought of exercise actually becomes appealing and it's as if you are getting younger . . . it's almost as if you experienced a fat body so that you could really appreciate your new life in a fit, healthy body . . . having to eat sweets to make life sweet is no longer where you're at . . . you are in La Dolce Vita.'

For the junk food eater
'Now that you recognise you have every right to a wonderful life, you are looking at the quality of your life . . . it is true that someone in a good state of mind can cope with any possible situation . . . a good state of mind, though, can be undermined by a poor lifestyle . . . lack of sleep and poor diet can easily affect the state of mind. You are becoming aware

that a poor diet is like buying cheap, second-hand oil for a racing car engine . . . it's a false economy.

'In your case "you are what you eat" . . . you already know that the human body and brain function best on a varied, balanced diet with plenty of fresh food . . . the quality of life comes out of choice . . . eating one type of food only is a habit, like an addiction . . . it may satisfy some short-term craving at the expense of depriving the body of important minerals and vitamins.

'Just as you would not choose the same holiday destination every year, when it comes to food variety really is the spice of life . . . junk food can be addictive, purely because it's so heavily advertised, so available and convenient . . . it is all too easy to snack and binge on . . . and to treat the retail outlet as your surrogate kitchen . . . the convenience of not cooking and not washing up shortens the time you spend involved with thinking about what exactly you are living on.

'When you prepare your own food, you make it the way you want it . . . it will be of good quality and will be different each day . . . because you want a healthier life, you take the time to choose what you eat, where you eat . . . and really to enjoy the experience of receiving your nourishment . . . you know that junk food is bad but, like a drug, it can be abused. Now, as you claim your life you choose sensible eating habits . . . because you recognise that you're worth it . . . a healthy body, healthy mind and a life of quality.'

For the male overweight drinker
'It's a fantastic feeling to be the master of your own destiny
. . . now, with the wisdom you've gained you've made the
most important decision of your life . . . you have no longer
got to be "one of the boys" . . . you've chosen to be a man
in your own right . . . an individual, not a sheep . . . you do
things because they are right for you, not because your
mates will approve.

'You've also taken a good look at the way you live your
life and the way you look . . . you have noticed that people
who drink have the usual pot belly and that you are no
exception . . . the oestrogen in the beer helps men's
pectorals to look more like breasts and the overall effect of
the drinking is a lower sperm count! . . . you know that
now is the time to reclaim your virility and regain the
physique that is rightly yours.

'It takes a real man to say "no" . . . but you are now
certain which way you want your life to go . . . no longer
will you drink alcohol just to make someone else feel good
about drinking . . . moderation and common sense are
what distinguish you from those who don't recognise the
effects of regular boozing . . . it also sets you apart from
those too weak to do anything about it . . . to make such
clear changes in your lifestyle is truly inspiring and very
quickly your friends learn to respect your choice.

'The more you respect yourself, the easier you find it, to
respect others . . . a characteristic that women find very
attractive . . . it also makes you easy to get on with . . . this
attribute is profoundly changing your life for the better . . .
you are drinking far less, not indulging in bar snacks and

no longer propping up the bar . . . you have got outside interests that keep you fit and out of the smoky pub atmosphere for most of the time . . . your life has found a new meaning doing the things that you really want to do . . . your weight is coming down steadily and safely . . . your body feels lighter and everything smells fresher as you regain your zest for life . . . welcome to your new life.'

For the comfort eater
'Comfort eating is like an addictive drug . . . you are on a short "high" when you satisfy your craving but it then leads to a vicious circle, where you get hooked . . . this habit seeks out people who are currently stressed, needy of love, attention or thrills . . . the eating is a substitute for the real thing . . . rather than going out and meeting real people or taking part in a real activity, you swallow some food . . . it is a temporary fix only, because afterwards there are no new friends . . . you've not done anything new and interesting and you are still stressed . . . so when the fix wears off, the urge to be satisfied returns . . . another fix . . . more food . . . more weight.

'Sometimes, being slightly overweight or shy in the first place may have contributed to the situation . . . the comfort eating only makes things worse . . . the bigger you get, the less you want to go out . . . you're burning fewer calories because you're doing less but you're eating more . . . you get fatter . . . it just keeps getting worse.

'JUST STOP! . . . Put an end to this silliness . . . claim back your life . . . if you get an urge to eat, drink a glass of water and then go out and do something . . . visit friends

. . . go for a walk . . . go places where you can meet people and get involved with the living . . . leave behind the old you, the hard-done-by couch potato . . . As your lifestyle changes, you'll be receiving love, attention and respect . . . and you will no longer feel the urge to eat outside normal meal times . . . you begin to eat to live and no longer live to eat.'

For the protection eater
'When you put on weight to protect yourself, it may be because you believe that larger people are less likely to be physically attacked . . . you also become more bulky, looking less attractive . . . this fear of attack or unwanted sexual advances may have stemmed from warnings and stories that have now grown out of all proportion to their usefulness . . . on the other hand, this fear may have stemmed from a past experience which you do not wish to repeat.

'Either way, time has moved on . . . you are wiser now . . . there are better ways of dealing with this . . . certainly, better than hiding behind an unhealthy layer of fat . . . in any event, fat is certainly not always unattractive or unsexy and, therefore, this protection is not foolproof . . . usually, the people who attack others are insecure and believe themselves to be cowards . . . they attack people trying to convince themselves of their own power . . . they are too scared to attack someone who looks confident . . . they prefer to attack those who look timid, lost or weak . . . in fact, a victim.

'Irrespective of your size, if you go about confidently, with a sense of purpose, you will not make yourself a target

. . . *actual violence is very rare and unlikely to happen to you once you have left school . . . you prepare your journeys properly and always check alternative travel arrangements . . . do not let fear stop you from living your life . . . F-E-A-R means Fantasies Envisaged As Real . . . negative fantasies are the source of all fear . . . the reality of any situation is what you respond to . . . fear is irrational and the only response to it is stress, and more fear.*

'*Instead, visualise positive outcomes . . . always create happy endings . . . you are the director in your own life story . . . the more you do this, the more your life becomes directed, and people will respect you even more . . . self-respect is the key to warding off unwanted sexual attention . . . being able to assert your wishes clearly early on prevents misunderstandings and situations getting out of hand . . . it is that simple . . . know what you want and state it . . . it is your right.*

'*Remember, "Don't ask – Don't get," and not saying no is as good as saying yes . . . it's your body . . . nobody has any rights over it other than you . . . never focus on the things that you don't want . . . in life you'll get what you believe you deserve.*'

For the punishment eater
'*In life, everybody makes mistakes . . . no-one is perfect . . . learn the lesson and get on with your life . . . that's it . . . simple . . . guilt is a total waste of time . . . guilt is a monument that we build to show that we made a mistake . . . no-one gave you the planning permission . . . you just took it on . . . it becomes the burden of your life.*

'No mistake is so important that your life should be shortened because of it . . . we learn from our mistakes . . . just learn the lesson . . . your experience is important . . . share what you've learned so that others might not make the same mistake . . . making yourself fat and unlikable doesn't help you and it doesn't help the people around you.

'Turning yourself into a blob is a reflection of your poor self-image . . . the standards you have set yourself are too high and you can now learn to forgive yourself . . . you are human after all and humans make mistakes . . . we all have good intentions but they're not always based on reality. When we fail to live up to our own intentions, there is no need to entertain guilt . . . all you have to do is read just what you know is achievable with your available time and skills.

'Learn to value your time . . . do not make promises that you cannot keep . . . be completely honest with others and yourself . . . before the event . . . then there can be no upsets. Guilt is about living in the past . . . let it be . . . the joy in your life comes from where you are , in the "now" . . . live in the present . . . it's the only place to be happy.'

4

CASE HISTORIES

This chapter is based on case histories – on some of my clients who, through hypnosis, have found the root cause of their problems. With this new information to hand, the conscious mind has been able to change their behaviour permanently. It's a little bit like a jigsaw: you can't finish it if some of the parts are missing. Included in this chapter are a couple of case histories that are not connected to weight loss; however, the two cases in question are excellent examples that show the complexities of the mind and, I believe, will help you to understand why being overweight is not as cut and dried as people tend to believe.

For the person who has never had a weight problem, the 'Eat less and you lose weight' philosophy is the simple answer. But if it were that easy for everyone, I wouldn't need to write this book and the billion-pound weight reduction business would not be such a lucrative concern. So, this chapter is based on showing you why the overweight can have such problems in following what would seem, at first glance, to be the simple formula of merely eating less.

The hidden information that can be uncovered by hypnosis can be so incredible that you really have to be present at a therapy session to experience the emotions and witness the extraordinary complexity of the mind. I have demonstrated live therapy in front of hardened businessmen who have been in tears as the subject's memories are released. These forgotten emotions pour out of the subject and seem to create a natural sympathy with whoever is present. The common denominator is that afterwards the audience invariably say they feel privileged to have been part of such a moving experience. The subject also feels a closeness to whoever else is in the room at the time; whether it be a small group or a hundred people, a bonding is experienced. It is a type of bonding that can be seen in healing or a shared religious experience and is very potent for all present.

I have worked with and trained many psychologists in hypnosis. What I found to be very consistent was that, although they had had expert training and a wonderful background in how the mind is supposed to work, as well as being privy to all the latest research findings, they seemed to have one thing in common: they tended to miss the sheer basics of the actual workings of the mind, unfortunately forgetting that the inner mind is not logical – or 'logical' as we know it. The hypnotherapist, however, is constantly working with these peculiarities of behaviour and it becomes second nature to him or her. Psychologists believe they understand but they rarely get the chance to observe deep trance and regression and the answer might be to include a more proficient hypnosis training in their syllabus. It only takes a week to learn, while psychology takes years. Therapy in hypnosis is a short cut that cannot be equalled.

A psychologist friend of mine who recently explained that she had spent hours analysing herself and checking why she had a certain unpleasant thought pattern that she could not change came up with a conclusion that was logical to her but it did not change her behaviour. She had spent a great deal of time analysing my behaviour so that I was nearly sold on all the sophisticated words and complicated structure of her science. She explained that when I lost my memory I was attention-seeking. So when every now and again it reared its head – my memory loss, that is – it was for the same reason, to gain attention. Gosh, I spent years having to listen to this conclusion by nearly everyone I met, none of whom had had a training in psychology! In my view, this showed her lack of understanding of the peculiarities of the subconscious.

I believe that the answer is always in our complex and buried memories of which we have no conscious memory. If the memory which was the source of the problem was accessible to the conscious, then the problem would not exist at all because it would have been worked out by the conscious. Hypnotherapy is the only form of treatment that can get to the root and bring forward the answers, so that the repairs can take place naturally. What seems to happen is that if we use the inner mind (or subconscious) to find the missing pieces, the jigsaw problem can then be completely solved.

I know, without any doubt, that if I have a problem that needs solving, I would have no choice but to seek another advanced hypnotherapist to guide me to find the deeply buried information and to bring this information forward so that my conscious mind is aware of it; then the logical process of solving and healing can take place. Indeed, it is only this year that I have discovered there is another option – that of Hypno-Sleep.

What complicates the issue more is that if the

111

hypnotherapist is not versed in new and quick methods, it could take for ever to find the source of the problem. However, thanks to new technology and computerisation, new training methods have developed and cut the therapy time to as little as three to five one-hour sessions, instead of twenty. The psychologist is trained to work in a completely different way, often taking many lengthy sessions. Much of their training is based on theory, which can be very time-consuming and not always accurate. The hypnotherapist gets right to the root of the problem and brings it forward – which in turn helps the client to deal with this fresh information – by basic mind techniques. The psychologist analyses the thinking structure and uses a much more complex procedure.

Having said this, when a psychologist and a hypnotherapist work together on a deeply disturbed patient it can be exciting and very rewarding. The two sciences can complement each other extremely well. For example, once when I was working out of a private hospital, I needed the specialised psychologist to get me out of trouble when my remarks were taken out of context. I may not have known I had caused a problem, had we not been working together.

In this instance, I was working with a man who had a compulsion disorder which made him want to wash his hands constantly. He would take an hour and a half to shower and another fifteen minutes to wash his hands. He did this at very regular intervals through the day. Usually, this sort of compulsion stems from a death or a fear of someone close dying, when the subject makes a mental promise to themselves, such as: 'If my father lives, I will always be tidy/clean.' This simple promise can create a program after the fact. It doesn't always necessarily make a difference if the person lives or dies for the program to become fixed. This new program becomes fixed because it has been created in shock, without the logic of the conscious mind which was otherwise occupied. Reason has not been involved and so the behaviour becomes exaggerated and peculiar.

The gentleman in question had other trauma-related problems and was deeply depressed. I managed to make some headway, so that he was able to spend only fifteen minutes in the shower and a few minutes washing his hands. This was a great achievement. As he improved, I suggested that any time he wanted to see me on a casual basis, he could pop into my Harley Street office. This was just a gesture that I thought would build his ego. Instead, because he still had compulsive ideas, he worried that I would be offended if he didn't come to see me. What was on my part a harmless remark to a normal, healthy person had become a major problem to him. However, my psychologist colleague was able to deal with his problems much more easily now that major changes had already been made. Deeply disturbed people can benefit greatly from the harmony of both the medical and complementary sciences working together.

I treated a lady (whom I will call Jane) who was extremely overweight – at least twenty-two stone. She came to me when I was working in Scotland. Her husband had seen me for insomnia and now he was sleeping 'like a baby', she remarked. She had been overweight all of her life, starting out as a very fat child. Her marriage was reasonably happy but she hated being fat. When she was regressed in hypnosis to the very first time that she ate when she was not hungry, she told me that she had fallen in the bathroom and hurt herself. Her mother was putting some disinfectant on her knee, which she had cut quite deeply as she had fallen. She was crying hysterically and her mother was trying to calm her. Subsequently, her mother carried her downstairs and gave her some of her favourite chocolates. This took little Jane's mind off the pain.

I then regressed her to the next time she ate because she was upset. She had been hurt again when a playmate had accidentally kicked her and run away. Jane felt both the pain and the rejection by her playmate. This time, she had an urge to eat some chocolates which were in her lunch box. The pain was relieved and her playmate came round to apologise. These were only small traumas but both had occurred while she was shocked and now the program was set.

It was a very unusual program. Her inner mind believed that instead of the disinfectant healing her knee, the chocolate had achieved it. And when she was in need of help again, once more the chocolate had solved the problem. Thus, when in future she encountered problems, she had an urge to eat sweet things. This program was changed by simple techniques while in hypnosis. She was then able to diet and lose weight. She lost five stones gradually and safely within a few months.

I treated a young girl of fourteen years old, whose father had brought her to see me, suffering from bulimia. She looked fine and healthy and had a nice trim figure. Her father told me she had recently started to get obsessed with food and every change of shape in her body. Bodily changes were quite normal at her age but she believed she was grotesque. She had become withdrawn and the whole family was worried about her.

She told me she did not know why but she felt she had to eat and eat constantly. The only way for her to be able to counteract this problem was to make herself sick by sticking her fingers down her throat. She was aware that she was damaging herself but it seemed the only alternative.

In regression, she went back to a time when she was watching television. She was about twelve years old and watching a documentary-type film about a girl who had had anorexia and the horrors she went through in hospital. At the time she was watching this programme, my client was very vulnerable. She had been ill and was still very weak. At the same time, her mother and father were having a domestic fight while she watched the TV programme. The combination of the programme, her illness and her parents' squabble shocked her and her mind suffered a kind of overload. The programme stayed in her mind and she started to worry about becoming anorexic.

Later, when her body started to change in puberty and turn into more of a womanly shape, her mind took this on board as extra weight. Her fear triggered off the fear of being anorexic. So, her inner mind/subconscious developed a new strategy – making sure she ate so she wouldn't develop anorexia, yet still making sure she didn't put weight on by forcing herself to be sick. The problem wasn't so much the result of vomiting but the persistent voice inside her head telling her to eat constantly. Once this was rectified, there was no need for her to put her fingers down her throat and she could begin to eat in a more conventional and healthy way. The girl only remembered the TV programme after being regressed in hypnosis. She had no knowledge of the damaging programme beforehand but later she was able to piece the jigsaw together in a way which now made sense.

I have found that many a problem has occurred as a result of watching a programme on television that has disturbed the mind when it was in a particularly vulnerable state. It is only now being proved beyond doubt that TV programmes can be damaging to a vulnerable mind. I predicted this in my column when I was editor of a section of a magazine dealing with video and cable television in California, way back in 1980. It took ten years for my view to be accepted.

At this point I am going to include a case history which, although it has absolutely nothing to do with weight loss, allows you to see how an unwanted but factual mental program can be set early in life and become a permanent bad fixture in your make-up.

A hypnotherapist colleague had a client who was so frightened of cats that she would have heart palpitations and large red blemishes would appear on her arms if she even sensed a cat was present. She had developed an extra-sensory perception that told her if a cat was in as much as another part of the house. When her symptoms appeared, she knew that there was a cat in the vicinity and she was always proved right. She had lived with this dreadful phobia, as far as she knew, all of her life. It had only come to a head when she had fallen in love and was engaged to be married to a man whose mother owned two cats. Her only choice was either to get the phobia treated or never visit her mother-in-law-to-be. Of course, this latter course would have caused considerable friction in the future, especially if she had children.

Phobias are usually easily treated with hypnosis and so she came to my colleague with her troubles. Her symptoms indicated that it was probably trauma-related. The heart palpitations of fear and the nervous blotches could have been caused by a shock some time in her past, obviously very early in childhood, as she had always had these problems.

In regression therapy, she was instructed to go to the first time she had a fear of cats. It turned out to be when she was in her pram. You may find this surprising but the memory can easily regress to such early experiences. When I began my practice, I would always take my clients back to when they first walked, just to prove that this was an experience that they wouldn't have normally remembered. It never failed – everyone was able to do this. As my client reconstructed her experience, she was dozing in her pram when a frightening crack of thunder shocked her awake, causing her heart to beat very fast, like palpitations. Simultaneously, a cat had been frightened and jumped from a hedge over her pram. The thunder was still rolling as she opened her eyes, so her mind fused the noise of the thunder with the sight of the cat. This memory had stayed with her all her life and had been responsible for her fear of cats ever since!

Earlier in my career, I did a demonstration of hypnosis in front of about thirty-four Harley Street medical professionals. They included psychiatrists, psychologists, plastic surgeons and dentists. From this successful demonstration I was invited to be a consultant to a private hospital – very unusual for a hypnotherapist. From this demonstration, I also was lucky enough to have patients recommended to me by plastic surgeons.

I was introduced to a beautiful model whom I shall call Carol. She was admitted to a private hospital after trying to commit suicide. She had had her nose altered by one of the top plastic surgeons but she complained she didn't like it and asked for it to be done again. It was. However, she hated the new work just as much. She thought everyone was looking at her and she felt ridiculous, a laughing stock. Her problem was compounded by the fact she had put on weight through this ordeal and the plastic surgeon used this as an excuse to postpone further work on her nose. She was now in a dilemma, for the over-eating which had caused her face to become a little more chubby prevented the nose re-construction she desperately felt she needed. The more effort she put into losing weight, the more she seemed to fail.

Carol had been recommended to me by a plastic surgeon I will call Dr Brown. He explained that the nightmare of the plastic surgeon is the person who has work done on their face and cannot then accept the results. There is nothing wrong with the work but the patient believes there is. It's rather like the anorexic who thinks they are fat when, in reality, they look as if they have been in a concentration camp. They have been fooled by their own mind. It can become so serious that the patient is obsessive enough to attempt suicide, as Carol had done. Dr Brown explained that, although this is very uncommon, when it does happen it is a serious problem.

Reputable surgeons are aware of the signs of this type of phobia and would be alerted. More than likely, they would phone the original surgeon to check on the facts and probably make excuses to delay treatment. But Dr Brown's main worry was that Carol would go to different plastic surgeons – there are countless to choose from in the Harley Street area – and find one who was unscrupulous and who would agree to operate.

Carol had a very unusual overweight problem but her misinterpretation of her appearance had to be solved first, then the weight problem would just fade away. As a matter of fact, she didn't look at all overweight, but in her profession extra weight was a handicap. She also was very beautiful and her nose looked perfect. It was only because of her own belief system that she felt she looked repulsive – a nose of any shape would have caused her a problem.

Unfortunately, the person who develops this type of surgical phobia cannot be categorised. It applies not just to the neurotic person. When the phobia is set, the victim will beg, bribe and, if they have the money, pay fortunes to plastic surgeons to tempt them to operate. But, whatever the results, they are never satisfied and end up looking like what they most fear – ugly and ravaged and eventually beyond repair.

The work in hypnosis with Carol took about seven sessions before she was cured and she wrote a ten-page letter to thank me for the help. She was able to return to her career and accept her appearance.

I had a client (whom I will call Anne) who was an actress who did a bit of stripping on the side when the going got tough. She came to see me about her anorexic weight disorder. Anorexia is not always caused by having a weight problem. There is a danger of becoming anorexic if you stop wanting to eat for other reasons. It can happen after a broken love affair, for instance. When you stop eating, your body receives different instructions and food can taste just like sawdust. It then becomes an ordeal to eat at all, becoming a vicious circle. The more you don't eat, the more you don't want to. The body becomes thin and you then start to lose weight off your main storage areas, such as hips and arms, and most serious, the rear.

Anne was full of confidence and a lovely, jovial personality. Her figure, now looking somewhat thin, was very important to her. She was reaching her mid-thirties but expected to look like a teenager still. Her sights were set too high and, therefore, she was in constant conflict with herself, starving herself and going on outlandish diets. Each time she tried one of the so-called 'miracle' diets, she would be completely committed and believe that this was the one for her. A few months later, she would change her mind and be back to square one. She ate only small amounts of food and she now looked emaciated.

It transpired that her problem had stemmed from her mother. Anne believed that she had never been loved. She had no memory of her mother cuddling her or being anything but cruel to her. In regression, I had difficulty in finding even one happy occasion involving her mother. I remembered a technique I had used before with another girl who also couldn't find a happy memory with her mother. In hypnosis, I was able to regress her right back to when she was a baby and she recalled her mother cuddling her. I believed that however bad the mother had been, there would surely have been *one* occasion when she showed some form of love.

Fortunately, there had been one such instance and Anne was able to remember and feel the love that her mother had for her as she had cuddled her at this special moment. Other work was needed to build her self-image, which helped to pull her out of her anorexia. She later told me that although she still didn't like her mother, she had subsequently been able to be civil to her and not constantly argue. This was quite a new experience and now she could at least get on with her mother in a civilised way. The latent memory had helped her.

I teach my clients that if they want to change someone's attitude towards them, they need to change their own reactions first. This case was a very good example. Anne's change in attitude to her mother resulted in her mother responding more naturally and, although there was still no love lost between them, at least a more acceptable situation now existed. The anorexia was just a symptom of self-abuse because Anne didn't believe she was lovable. The ultimate problem had to be resolved before even attempting to deal with the weight disorder.

To illustrate further, whenever someone has an alcohol problem, the reason for the person having such a crutch has to be addressed before the alcohol abuse corrects itself.

Many of my clients have suffered from total rejection by their mother or fathers, or even both, and it has caused them to lose their self-respect or self-image and, therefore, they tend to abuse themselves. They subconsciously believe that 'if my parents don't love me, I must be unlovable, and, therefore, don't deserve happiness'. So many of these victims of their parents become victims of abuse from others, such as wives who are beaten by their husbands.

Anne was a victim of her family and that problem had to be

solved before she was able to come to terms with her weight problem. She was very intelligent but her behaviour was illogical and gave the indication of a trauma-related problem.

This sort of family rejection can lead to untold horrors and the victim, if already a little unbalanced, can end up committing terrible crimes. The Jersey murders, in which two brothers were involved in the killing of their parents, apparently arose from a lack of parental love. Where terrible violence has evolved, resulting in tragedy, it is often an example of retarded emotional rejection. These deep-rooted, trauma-related problems can be just as much part of a weight disorder as the simpler ones.

I remember that a few years ago I believed my tummy was not flat enough and asked my doctor how I could lose weight in that part of my body. I was thirty at the time. He looked at me and said that in some people fat congregates around certain areas when they pass twenty. Thighs and hips are key places but obviously mine was on my stomach. He added that, seeing as I was fit and ate healthily, I would have to do Jane Fonda-type work-outs every day, just to lose that small excess. He then looked me straight in the eye and asked: 'Is it worth it?'

His remark brought me to my senses. I realised that, indeed, my tummy was only slightly rounded. But I was looking for perfection. When I thought about it, I realised it certainly wouldn't be worth the effort of such a rigorous exercise regime to lose that slight roundness. When I look back, it seems ridiculous that I even bothered. I was very slim anyway but, like lots of young women, I had forgotten that you automatically become more rounded when you pass your teenage years. I was simply being influenced by the magazine models.

I had a friend who had a face lift operation which looked wonderful. A few years later she still looked stunning but said she was worried about her neck, which now didn't match her face. If she then had her neck done, would she not also look at her skin on her arms and her tummy? In fact, she looked marvellous. But we are never satisfied with ourselves. When nowhere near perfect, we are striving for improvement and when near-perfect we are still striving for perfection! *Does it ever end?*

5

MORE IS NOT BETTER . . .

Exercises and diets that can work when you have changed your attitude with hypnosis

This chapter is aimed at giving you some simple tips for either losing weight or for keeping your body trim when you have lost that extra weight. Unfortunately, when instructions are given, very few people actually follow them through scrupulously. There are some people who think 'more is better', and add on extra for good measure, especially when exercising, misguidedly thinking that this actually quickens the process. And, conversely, there are those who do less and think they can get away with it.

With isometrics, the extra exercises can strain the body and defeat the object. In fact, it can be quite unhealthy and prevent the specially designed exercises from being effective. Equally, with the balanced diet, adding or subtracting amounts of foods from it simply unbalances the carefully constructed plans. It's not surprising then that the results will not be to lose weight as promised but, more likely, to be up and down, gaining and losing on the roller-coaster existence of the perpetual dieter. The imbalance confuses the messages from the metabolism to the brain and so an illogical behaviour can be the result.

For example, when a person is carrying extra water retention, the message sent to the brain is to eat more. The extra eating can become quite obsessional, causing a constant conflict in the mind resulting from such a quandary. The unfortunate victim of water retention, especially if the water retention is a side effect of taking pills, like the birth pill or HRT, is left constantly thinking about eating and struggling not just to be slim but to prevent themselves gaining even more weight.

Overdoing even the non-fattening part of a balanced diet – for example, piling the plate with heaps of tomatoes or beetroot – will ensure the diet is no longer balanced. Even worse, when it comes to isometric exercising to add just a few extra seconds to a ten-second programme can be damaging or counteract the good you may have done, defeating the object. Remember more is not necessarily better.

I am the type of person who follows exactly to the letter what I am told to do and I have benefited in both my health and as a leading hypnotherapist because of this. If I had decided to impose my own version on to the methods I was taught in hypnosis before I was skilled enough to have the experience, I would have probably ended up a mediocre therapist. Instead, I followed the techniques and learnings of the masters precisely, knowing that they had taken years to develop their strategies. I knew I would only be able to develop my own ideas after a great deal of hands-on experience in the front line. That is, after dealing with hundreds of clients.

I learned how important it was to follow instructions precisely very early in life and this was compounded by my success. When I was only a teenager I developed a varicose vein in my left leg. I was shattered because it looked so ugly but, even worse, I suffered terrible pain. It was difficult for me to stand for any amount of time. In fact, I did the washing up kneeling down on a chair. After several months of this awful situation and after pestering the doctor, I heard there was a new treatment on the market. The vein was injected which killed the ugly blemish, resulting in its disappearance, and the constant ache was also eliminated.

The instructions from the hospital where I had been treated were to keep tight elastic bandages on for five weeks. I was strongly advised not to remove them at all. They had wrapped my legs from thigh to toe in these uncomfortable and very unattractive bandages and I had to walk three miles every day.

This was in the pioneering days of such injections for varicose veins and the pain was excruciating. I hadn't been told about the pain beforehand and it was so bad I thought that I had become infected. Because of my fear, I made sure I walked the three miles a day. I had never liked any form of exercise, so this was quite a feat for me. Each day I would drag myself to walk those three miles and sometimes it was so painful that tears would be rolling down my face as I walked.

This was in the days of the mini skirt and, like most teenagers, I was vain and so persevered. Within the year, the vein had disappeared and so had the pain. Now, coincidentally, my girlfriend also suffered the same problems with veins in her legs and she, like me, also decided to have the injections. But unlike me, she concluded that she already walked three miles a day while running around after her toddler. She deluded herself with this explanation and so did not follow the instructions given. Her problem veins are still with her to this day and her doctor would probably think the injections hadn't worked. However, in my view the reason was because she hadn't followed the all-important directions. In her mind, she had done what she had been asked. I also had a toddler at the time but still walked those extra gruelling three miles a day and it certainly worked for me, probably because I did as I was advised.

I see similar situations in my practice all the time, when the slimmer assures me that they do not eat a lot but still put on weight. My answer to this is that there were no fat people in the concentration camps! Then I proceed to get the real story of my client's eating behaviour. This remark is not just to remind them that you have to eat to gain weight or stay fat but a reminder for me also. It always amazes me what an excellent salesman the overweight person can be. They can look me straight in eye and assure me how little they eat – but their minds have carefully edited the truth. Of course, the average overweight person knows only too well how much they eat. This is just a part of the problem of the overweight . . . a problem that hypnosis can deal with.

One lady who was about two stones overweight came for treatment when I was practising on the beautiful island resort of Langkawi in Malaysia. The setting played an important part, as very hot weather usually makes the appetite subside. She said she hardly ate at all. In fact, she only had one meal a day – and that was a salad at lunchtime – and did not eat any other time except for an occasional ice cream with her children. This lady, whom I will call Jane, was so adamant about her eating habits it made me question my judgement – maybe I was wrong.

In hypnosis, I instructed her to picture herself with her normal helping of lunch and to imagine she took this plate of food into the kitchen. I then asked her to imagine she had to dish out to guests portions from her plate, portions that would then be served to guests for lunch as an average serving in an elegant restaurant. When she had completed this task in her imagination, I then asked her how many other plates her one plate had filled. To my amazement, her usual lunch plate had adequately filled three other average servings. Added to which was the news that she piled ready-made dressings on this enormous plateful of salad, which negated any good effects of the supposedly healthy eating, filling the system with generous amounts of fat and synthetics hidden in the supposedly innocent dressings.

When she came out of hypnosis she was amazed. She hadn't realised how much she had been stuffing into her system. She had almost fooled me, as she had fooled herself, into believing she ate very little. She had developed a trauma-related eating problem. Her system didn't like the one meal a day; it was overloaded and wasn't able to function naturally.

She explained she wasn't able to eat in the evening – she would be physically sick if she did – because of a bad experience she had suffered when she was a child. So, she served her children and her husband with their food but could not join them. This compounded her problem, alienating herself from them at dinner time, and her behaviour was affecting her whole family. She was very worried about her children, who were developing eating problems of their own as a result of her unusual eating. Retraining her eating habits was a major breakthrough and would help her children for the future. The trauma, causing the fixation of only one meal a day, which was clearly not working, had to be dealt with before the suggestion in hypnosis and a new pattern could emerge.

Many eating problems have been passed down to children, so the children grow up with eating disorders caused by their parents' bad habits, rather than their own personal traumas. In the case of children, suggestion hypnosis would normally have a better success rate than that of their parents. But now, with this new Hypno-Sleep there is another avenue to explore, an exciting breakthrough which allows suggestions to work even in trauma-related cases.

It is the same in both dieting and exercising. It is no use being given special, carefully planned instructions if you decide to interpret them in your own way. With this in mind, please do not spoil all your efforts by doing more than recommended; less is not good in exercising but at least it isn't harmful.

Why exercising is so important
Exercising is the most successful regenerating process we have. The older we get, the more we need to exercise. I found that I had talked myself into the idea that the thickness that had developed around my own waist in the last couple of years was due to my age. When I was researching this book, I needed to practise what I was about to preach and it worked even more than I anticipated. If I achieved nothing else in writing this book, I am delighted to say that I restored my figure. It also proved a very important point to me, namely that I was ignoring common sense. I now feel wonderfully alive because I am fitter, healthier and slimmer. If my body gets thicker around the waist again I will have no-one to blame but myself.

How you can take the time and effort to exercise
Exercising is very important but the overweight person finds it almost impossible to appropriate the energy if they are already feeling lethargic, as they will by carrying all that extra load. Imagine that for every extra ten pounds of weight you are carrying, you tie a ten-pound bag of potatoes around your waist. In your imagination, see how many sacks you are carrying and then picture yourself taking one or even a few bags of potatoes away and imagine how much more agile you would be. Simply crash dieting will unbalance your body even more and the flesh will just hang because you have not compensated with muscle toning and tightening. So, you have no option but to change your eating habits as well as to exercise, for one directly affects

129

the other. You cannot divorce the body from the mind.

Stimulate your energy level with healthy eating, while exercising will tone up and freshen up your muscles and body. You will begin to look younger and fresher, your face will lose that dull pallor, your hair will lose that dullness and your nails will stop splitting – all of which are very significant signs of bad eating habits. Eventually, you will have retrained your body and mind and the food requests to your brain will begin to change and a healthier food will be chosen, with just as much enjoyment as the rich, stodgy, junk food you may have wanted in the past. But it doesn't happen overnight. This is where hypnosis suggestions are extremely important in speeding up the process and in changing your attitude so that you want to eat in a healthy way and treat your body to some good exercise as a perk, rather than a punishment.

When you are young, generally you are full of energy and tend to dash about. If you aren't as young as you used to be, then you need to stimulate your metabolism into working at maximum efficiency with exercises. The older you get, the more you need to exercise your limbs. 'What you don't use, you lose!' is an old saying and very true. Your body can develop ailments and diseases, such as arthritis, later on in life if you don't keep your muscles toned.

The best exercise you can have is to walk briskly for half an hour at least three times a week. Doing it every day is better, building up to an hour, but this has to be in association with a healthy lifestyle. Think about your body, care for it, treat it with the respect it deserves, otherwise don't be surprised if it lets you down badly.

There are some excellent tread machines on the market that work for the person who cannot always get out for that walk. You step on the machine and you can walk as much and as fast as you desire. Bad weather, fear of walking alone or just not living in a suitable area for walking are reasons to think about this option. If you invest in some form of machinery, some tread machines are very sophisticated. The latest ones have a built-in sound system for your favourite music, useful because music that you enjoy helps keep the spring in your step. The mind likes a rhythm.

A doctor once told me that people are like dogs – they need regular walks to keep them fit. It is very unhealthy not to exercise an animal; in fact, it is thought of as cruel. But the tread machine is only a good alternative if you are going to use it. It's an expensive mistake if you are the type of person who tires of gadgets quickly!

Swimming is excellent, but be sensible. If you have your own pool, then ten lengths a day would be very beneficial, otherwise try to fit in a weekly visit to a public pool, building up to twenty lengths. When I lived in an apartment in the centre of London with a pool, I had a seventy-year-old neighbour who had become so obsessive about her daily swim that she would have withdrawal symptoms if she didn't do her thirty lengths a day. If the pool was closed for cleaning, she would be in an absolute panic. More, in her case, was certainly not better.

The formula
Hypnosis helps achieve the proven formula for losing

weight thus – D + E = WL (Diet plus Exercising equals Weight Loss) and that's guaranteed!

That is it – there's no magic. Hypnosis just prompts you to enjoy both dieting and exercising.

I am not claiming to be an expert on diet and exercising but I want to share with you some useful information I have come across and to be absolutely certain that it is workable, I have had this chapter supervised by experts. These tips are to help you on your way.

Fat is the body's way of storing extra food for emergencies such as famine. If you eat more calories than you need, the excess will form mainly around the stomach, thighs and top of the arms. Any form of exercise requires energy. The energy is accumulated from fat cells and the food you eat. If you exercise consistently or reduce your food intake each day, this set of circumstances will guarantee you losing weight.

Exercising will entice the metabolism to work faster. When you exercise, you will lose fat from all over the body, not necessarily just from the part of the body you are exercising. If you want to lose the flab from your tummy, it is not going to work just by focusing on lots of tummy exercises and nothing else. So, if you have said, 'I do lots of exercises and I still don't lose any weight,' this statement could be true. If you concentrate on one area of your body and exercise it like mad, all that will happen is a small amount of weight will come evenly off your body – so insignificant that it is unlikely that you will notice and therefore you cannot exercise only one part of your body enough to lose a lot of weight all round, as well as off the most offending area.

Of course, if you have no extra fat and only need a tummy toning, then you will see more results because you do not require to get rid of the all-round fat first. The rule is, whatever exercise you do will reduce your all-round fat and the concentrated extra exercises will start to reduce and tone up the problem areas like thighs and stomach. That is why it is so important to do general exercises like walking, swimming, cycling or skipping, which will force the metabolism to work at a higher rate than when you concentrate on a single set of muscles. You will start to see the result after a few weeks.

Be careful never to get the body into any position that will allow the back to arch incorrectly and always loosen up your body before you start. Begin by rolling your neck and moving your arms in a windmill swing, then stop, drop-bend over so that your arms are dangling near your toes and relax for a moment. Then stand with your feet together and tilt your body to one side as you slide your arm in a straight line down your leg as far as it will go. Draw yourself up to a straight position and do the same on the other side. Do this five times to loosen up

Your back is very important and if you have ever suffered from backache you will know the misery a weak back can cause. So, be sure to follow the instructions on exercising with care and check your chosen exercise routine with a trusted expert. If you don't know of one, check with two gyms for comparison – two is safer, as one may be wrong – or ask your doctor to recommend a specialist for advice. If unsure, never be afraid to ask. Remember, it's your life and your agony . . .

Droopy buttocks

It is a good idea to get into the habit of tightening up your buttock muscles for ten-second periods, three times a day. Remind yourself to do this exercise by getting into the habit when you are, perhaps, in a queue at lunchtime or before you eat a meal. I do three of the exercises (upper arms, tummy and buttocks) three times a day.

Pull your buttocks in tightly and hold for a slow count of ten, then release them. Also, walking on your buttocks across the room once a day is great for your posterior. It prevents that bottom droop. So many glamour-conscious people have felt they needed to have that surgical tuck for a droopy posterior when this simple exercise could have prevented it.

Tummy tightening

A flabby tummy is not a pretty sight for anyone. But you have to be careful what exercises you choose. The most popular exercises for the tummy for many years have been sit-ups and what is known as the Roman chair (an apparatus found in many gyms). I have been recommended never to practise them because they are ineffective and the sit-ups can lead to injury. It can produce strain on the lower back and pain in this area in later life.

A very simple firming exercise is using isometrics. If you are a driver, when you drive under bridges or stop at traffic lights, use this as a good trigger to remind you to pull in and tighten the muscles of your stomach – again for the count of ten, every day, three separate times a day. If you don't drive, use another reminder, such as when you make a cup of tea or answer the phone. Any of these tips have to be used with common sense. If you only answer the phone a few times a day, then this would be reasonable, but if you have a busy line your phone rings constantly, or alternately hardly at all, then this would be ridiculous.

Top arm flab
When you are walking through an open door, preferably at home, or when you are by yourself, just pause at the framework and extend your arms as if you are going to use all your weight to push the door frame apart. Let your arms become stiff and rigid, then, still keeping your arms rigid, push your arms out directly to the side of you, so that your palms are pressing the framework, pushing away sideways. Push as hard as you can and count slowly up to ten and then relax. Do this no more than three times a day, at separate times. This is such a simple exercise, but it will tighten up the muscles at the top insides of your arms. It helps to prevent the top of the under-arm sagging when you reach middle age, or if you are in this age group already, it will help firm up the flesh. It's also an area to keep check on when losing weight. If you have a lot of weight to lose and you have just been dieting but you haven't been exercising, your skin may have lost its elasticity. It will just hang loose, therefore it is very important to keep an eye on this area, otherwise it can look very unsightly.

Thigh firmness
Another important area of the body that needs attention when losing weight is the thighs, which can be very

unattractive if the flesh droops. Sit on a chair, wooden, straight-backed if possible, and put your feet together. Lift your legs up so that your knees are touching your chin, hold them in that position for a slow count of ten and then slowly drop them down. Also, stand up, feet together, and lift your knee up to your waist, clasp your knee and pull it up in front of you as far as you can towards your chest. Then hold that position for the count of ten. You should do this five to ten times, once a day.

Sit on the floor and stretch your inner thighs by sitting with your knees out to the sides of you and the soles of your feet touching. Ease your knees towards the floor by pushing your knees with your hands, with a gentle pressure as far as you can, and hold this position for the count of ten. Again, do this five to ten times, once a day.

Bust firming
Sit or stand up straight, shoulders back, and clasp your upper arms, just in front of your elbows. Then, with a firm grip push your skin towards the elbows and feel the pectoral muscles at the side of your bust firm up. Press to the slow count of ten; do this five to ten times, once a day.

A face lift
Stand up straight and push your head back as far as you can, stretching your chin, pull out your jaw and hold for ten seconds, again three times a day. Now your face – contort it in all sorts of weird positions, pulling your face and stretching it in all different positions. Hold each position for at least a second and finish by opening up

your mouth wide and stretching it.

A massage of the face will encourage the blood to flow just under the surface, stimulating the skin, working upwards from the mouth, up the cheeks, gently stroking the skin in a half circle out towards your ears, making sure not to stretch the skin directly under the eyes. A circular movement at the temples and forehead will stimulate the skin. Massage is a preventative method for ageing. Creams are a questionable method. It has been suggested that creams do little good. I must admit, I have not suffered from never using them but this is a delicate matter at the moment and still a bone of contention, with conflicting ideas. One authoritative figure seems to disprove the other, but markets and products change and maybe in the future there will be something that helps halt the ageing process.

An all-rounder quick burst of exercise
Running on the spot for a good minute will refresh you. Make sure you lift your knees up and run fast. Doing this two or three times a day certainly gives your heart a treat. An ideal time to begin is before breakfast and then have a slow stretch to loosen up the rest of your body. When I did an exercise routine with Dave Prowse, a former Mr Universe and well known for his role as Darth Vader in the film *Star Wars*, I was writing for a magazine on modelling and wanted to see the progress personally, so I attended his fitness centre in London. At the time, I hated all forms of exercise but work overload prevented me from completing the great programme. Dave Prowse explained that jogging was definitely not the answer. He told me that it was a

misconception that jogging (perhaps the most popular form of exercise for many people) was good for you. He believed that it doesn't increase the heartbeat enough and can actually put a strain on the heart, whereas a good run does increase the heartbeat to an acceptable level and a brisk walk is equally healthy. Walking doesn't actually increase the heartbeat, as running does, but at least there is no strain on the heart. Prowse pointed out to me that the man who invented this modern-day exercise of jogging, a Mr James, himself died on the job, as you might say, of a heart attack while jogging in 1984. Yet this unhealthy exercise is still as popular, with a whole fashionable industry attached to it.

If you like active exercising, the hoola-hoop – if you can find one today – or skipping are very energetic alternatives. But do not do either to excess if you haven't exercised for some time. Build up to a full regime slowly.

Tips for a healthy diet
Researches at Pepsi's labs in the USA have come up with a new soft drink. The drink is a fruit juice which stops people wanting to eat. The secret lies in the contents. It contains lots of citric acid, like strong lemonade. This tartiness is disguised with fruit flavouring and saccharine. Pepsi tried it out on a panel of people twenty minutes before they sat down to eat their main meal. The panel responded that the drink tasted like ordinary fruit juice but it resulted in them eating thirty per cent less of the meal than normal. But before you eagerly wait for this seemingly extraordinarily easy way out to come on to the market, just gather your thoughts and contemplate how it is made.

It has a practical purpose of cessation of the appetite with citric acid, which is then disguised as something more pleasurable. Hang on there, you can do this with hypnosis! You can actually instruct your mind to believe that a block of wood is a roast beef meal. The subject would smell the wood and the brain will have changed the messages so that he could actually smell the wonderful aroma of a roast beef dinner. To prove a subject is hypnotised, a little trick the hypnotist has up his sleeve is to get the subject to eat say a lemon while he is in hypnosis, after previously suggesting to him that it is an orange. The mind is fooled and the subject eats the lemon as if it is an orange. Usually, the hypnotist brings him out of hypnosis when he is in the middle of eating the lemon. As soon as the subject realises his mistake, he generally spits out the remaining lemon in his mouth and contorts his face as he actually now tastes the lemon. It has also been scientifically proved that we can produce in our bodies any drug known to mankind. This is produced by the mind and is similar to the subconscious switching on an illness, like my amnesia. The subject suffers the same side effects as if it was a true, physical illness rather than a trauma-related one.

Therefore, if we can produce a suggestion that certain foods will act like citric acid when consumed and that this is for the benefit of the subject, then there is no reason why the subconscious would not take this on board. So why risk the chemical imbalances to lose weight when, with some effort and practice, you can do it yourself . . . safely?

For the person who really hasn't much idea of healthy eating, or the new dieter, a few interesting tips can be a healthy start to a healthy life. I cannot stress enough how important it is to train children into healthy eating. This will shape not only their body in later life but enhance their lifestyle.

Look at the portion on your plate. Ignore the instructions that you can have as much as you like of one food because it is so low in calories. If you overload your plate, you are eating for more than one person and if you do this with each meal this will compound the problem. By the end of the day you will have eaten for two or even three people. You rarely see a trim person have to pile their plate high as if it's their last meal. The idea is to enjoy your meal but it's still only an interruption in your life, time put aside to refuel your system.

It is also important to be aware of the possibility that the fruits and vegetables we are eating may not hold all the vitamins that we need. A simple spraying of chemicals can eliminate the all-important vitamins and nutrients that we rely on; therefore, it is important to balance our food and have a variety. Your body will tell you if you are lacking in anything. Hair, teeth, nails and complexion will give you a good indication of a vitamin deficiency. Any excessive changes in your body can be due to you suddenly becoming allergic to a type of food.

Wheat and dairy products are frequently the cause of allergies. It may just be that you are eating too much of the offending food and you should cut down. Completely cutting it out can be irritating, too, as the body may become so allergic to the eliminated food that it rejects it altogether if you to try to reintroduce it into your diet. But this is really a trial-and-error situation. Generally, cutting down is sufficient. When I developed an allergy to milk, I realised it was because I was having café-au-lait (half milk and half water) four or five times a day. It overloaded my system and caused water retention, to which I tend to be prone. No more milky coffees was all that was needed.

It has been suggested that it is beneficial to have a half a grapefruit before your main meal to help the digestion, but sometimes this fruit is too citrous for some people. Eating pieces of fresh pineapple is a far better alternative, as it helps the intestinal track to digest and break up the fats. But it is best to eat it only half an hour before or after a meal for digestion.

In general, common sense is the orchestrator of a well-balanced diet. Don't stuff yourself with starch. A certain amount of roughage is necessary, however, for the wellbeing of your intestinal tract.

For good health it is best to start the day with something to eat. If you don't like eating in the morning and think that you will lose more weight than the person who does, you are very wrong. You need to eat first thing to get your metabolism working, even if it's only a piece of fruit. The old saying is correct: 'Breakfast like a king, lunch like a prince and dine like a pauper.' Unfortunately, many people miss out breakfast altogether, with no time to eat as they rush off to work after a coffee and perhaps a cigarette. This, of course, is courting disaster. You will have made three major mistakes! First, not having anything to eat ensures that your metabolism is sluggish. Also, the person who hasn't eaten breakfast is more likely to have a starchy bun or doughnut, coffee and maybe a cigarette at mid-morning break or the child to consume sweets. Second, apart from the obvious risk of cancer, the cigarette is polluting and damaging your body, leaving your body vulnerable to allergies and disease. Finally, coffee is not the best drink on an empty stomach and has no nutritional value.

For the coffee and fag brigade, stop! Sorry, but you need to start your metabolism and, so, if you don't have an appetite make sure you eat three types of fruit or even a natural yoghurt. Research has been done in the States that proved that the idea of a cigarette halting the appetite was a fallacy. It proved that smokers were more likely to be overweight than their non-smoking friends because cigarettes *slow down the metabolism*. So, change your habits – *NOW!*

If you do not eat breakfast, then your offspring may follow the pattern and it is very unhealthy to send a child to school without food. Their blood sugar drops and their mind is not as sharp for learning. In the morning, it is a good idea to give your intestines something to bite on, for the regularity of your bowels and for the working of your whole system.

If you are used to eating large fry-ups, then you have to stop. That is the diet for an early death. Certain foods are full of additives and preservatives which we have to avoid for a healthier eating regime. If you think you can occasionally have a fry-up, say at weekends, think again. To retrain your taste buds means a totally new way of eating. The longer you refrain from these potential heart-attack foods, the easier it will be to lose the taste for them.

You could choose to eat fruit (about three fruits, such as apples, bananas – a good source of potassium – and grapes) and you can add five ounces of plain yoghurt, preferably low-fat, with the right type of live bacteria. If you are rushing off to work, eat one piece of fruit and take the others to eat at the break. Of course, you can vary the fruits.

Certain fruits are better to eat in quantity than others. Strawberries, mango and pineapple are all acidic but, besides that, pineapple is an excellent aid to the digestion of your food. Bromine is a well-known digestive and is made from pineapple. Two slices of fresh pineapple eaten half an hour after each meal will help the digestion, particularly the fats. Papaya is a natural healing agent and is wonderful for breakfast or dessert. It is also quite filling.

You should choose to eat food which provides good roughage. Shredded wheat is top of the list because it doesn't include sugar, but don't spoil it by adding sugar. The shredded wheat acts like a little scrubbing brush, clearing your intestinal tract, cleaning it up and stopping blockages. Instead of having it with milk, try softening the cereal with natural fruit juice. Limit yourself to a quarter to a half pint of milk a day, including milk used on cereals. Porridge is a good breakfast because it lines the stomach and fills you up.

Drink a glass of water half an hour before you have a meal. Apart from it being very cleansing, it will take the edge off your appetite.

Diets should not make your life a misery. It is better to cut down on your intake of some foods rather than eliminate them, or you will find that you get very touchy about what you eat and that also can become another problem. Also, you may get a reaction if you try to introduce the food again. Of course, eating junk foods is just chemically abusing your body and can be completely eliminated. For a change for breakfast try herbal teas or Chinese tea. If you are really intending to look after your body you will be very strict with your coffee, tea, milk and butter/margarine intake. You can make your own yoghurt and a recipe is included on page 151.

Interesting ideas available on the market
Propolis is an extract from bees. It is used by the bee to clean itself and the hive. It is very precious and expensive because a litre can take six months to accumulate from reasonably-sized hives. Not all beekeepers have the know-how or realise its healing value, so there is not a great deal of public awareness about it. If a product includes propolis and is not too expensive, then the amount will be very small and unlikely to have a dramatic effect. To give an example, I would have to pay approximately £50 for a very small bottle that would last me for a month. It is really a rich person's supplement but has extraordinary healing powers and can very quickly balance your system. Used on the exterior of the body, the healing it brings about is unique. From the simple spot to severe burns, the healing time can be halved.

Although weight is not necessarily associated with healing, there are times when you would benefit from a healing programme. There is a machine on the market called

PEME (which stands for Pulsed Electro Magnetic Energy) that increases the healing process by around fifty per cent. It has been used for many years by diverse subjects ranging from royalty to polo horses. Its success with animals takes away the scepticism of it being merely a placebo. You may ask, what has healing to do with weight? The adrenal system can be boosted, helping your whole system to work more efficiently.

If you are someone who has had bulimia, then you will have probably ravaged your stomach by continually vomiting. If you're anorexic, you have starved your body and it is in a very bad shape and needs all the help it can get. Hypno-Sleep can help these disorders but then you have the aftermath to clear up – a badly abused body. The good news is that the body will heal when you get back into a healthy lifestyle. As to how much, it depends on how long and how much abuse it has had.

The meal of the day
The main meal of the day should be lunch. Unfortunately, this is not always possible. Also heavy lunches make you sleepy. In earlier times it was customary to have a nap after a large lunch. So be sensible and eat according to your lifestyle. If you are on an expense account and eat regularly in restaurants for lunch, then it is easy to order healthy meals. Just leave out the heavy sauces and fried foods and you will find that you no longer want them. Stick to an oil and vinegar dressing on salads and forget the mayonnaise.

Lunch suggestions
Try eating salad, with fish, like smoked mackerel (very inexpensive and filling), or chicken, meat, cheese or perhaps pasta – all are sensible for lunch. It is far better to make the lunch your main meal to help your digestion, but even your main meal should not be too heavy or it will affect your performance at work. The evening meal should be light. If you have problems with this, ask yourself how serious you are in wanting to diet. If you have a lot of weight to lose, then you are going to have to put more commitment into the whole procedure.

If you only have a small amount to lose, then you can probably just cut down and eat more healthily and still eat your main meal in the evening. You need to get used to a normal-sized plate with a normal portion. Never, never fill your plate up. It looks ridiculous and it will get you into bad habits of overloading yourself. Even if you choose salad, you are what you eat, and if your eating habits resemble a hog's, then you probably look like one to the onlooker.

Chinese tea is very refreshing and healthy with your meals. It tastes even better when you retrain your palate with fresher food and cut out all those thick rich sauces that are a disaster for healthy eating.

Light meal ideas (either lunch or dinner)
Salad Nicoise
   Ingredients:
   1 lettuce
   ½lb tiny cherry tomatoes

½lb cooked new potatoes
½lb cooked green beans
1 tin of tuna fish (in brine not oil)
1 tin of anchovies
Salad dressing:
4 tbspns of olive oil
2 tbspns of freshly squeezed lemon juice
a pinch of sugar and salt
Serves 4

One bowl of clear soup. Remember, just because its calorie count is virtually non-existent, don't pick a massive bowl and fill it to the brim. A normal serving will look very small to the overweight. If you replace the word 'normal' with 'dainty', it may help you when you are dishing up. For your second course, one wholemeal roll with two tomatoes and four ounces of cherries, displayed on a medium-sized plate.

Sandwich fillers with a difference
Tuna and mint: This is very easy to prepare. Open a tin of tuna (preferably in brine not oil), drain and add one teaspoon of mint sauce, mix together and add a dash of pepper, serve on one roll or two crispbreads. Cucumber and tomato are tasty additions. Have an apple or other fruit for dessert.

Jacket potato
8 oz baked potato filled with 3 oz of cottage cheese, baked beans or chilli. Chopped bacon, tomatoes, and sauces are

all useful fillers. Serve with salad and oil and vinegar dressing. I tend to prefer a simple oil and vinegar dressing, with a few herbs added to taste, because I am suspicious of anything that says 'fat-free', especially dressings – but that's a personal choice.

Stir-fry

You don't have to have a wok to make a very interesting and healthy stir-fry. Heat a deep frying pan, or wok, with a tablespoon of sunflower oil and a tablespoon of soy sauce (dark) and add the main ingredient – small strips of turkey, chicken or pork. Cook for at least ten minutes adding a chopped-up, medium-sized onion and a few slices of red, yellow and green peppers and fry together until cooked for approximately five minutes longer. You can add different spices, such as ginger, to add interest. Use a third of each pepper for one serving (the rest can be diced and used later with a salad or omelettes). Serve with rice.

Cheese and macaroni

This is very simple to prepare. Buy a packet of cheese sauce and some cheese, grate the cheese and melt into half a pint of milk. Serve with cooked macaroni pasta. Nice as a once-a-week, low-cost meal.

Liver and onions

Heat the onions in a non-stick frying pan without fat. Add the liver and ½ pint of vegetable stock, cook either on the top of the cooker or as a casserole until tender. Thicken with cornflour or gravy powder and serve with new potatoes, a green vegetable such as broccoli or cabbage and carrots.

Spaghetti Bolognese

A very filling and easy to prepare tasty dish. Serves four. One can of spaghetti sauce, one small can of tomatoes, one diced onion and 1¼ lbs of lean, minced beef (you can use mixed soya if you prefer not to eat red meat). Heat the beef and onions, then drain off all the fat. Then add to a medium pan with the rest of the ingredients. Complete with four bayleaves and crushed peppers. Simmer for half an hour and serve with boiled wholemeal spaghetti. Although you are using tinned foods, which are probably not as healthy, for a special occasion and as long as you keep your portion dainty, then it is still giving you a good balance.

Lancashire minced beef stew

Very easy to prepare and very acceptable for entertaining for the busy person. Ingredients: 1½lb of lean beef, one large onion, 6 small or 3 large carrots, a portion of a small swede, one large leek, 6 large potatoes, 1 stock cube, gravy browning and 1 tablespoon of cornflour to thicken, salt and pepper. (Serves four or can freeze for future dinners.)

When you are having guests and you are out at work by day, the advantage of this is you can prepare it the night before. Use a medium to large pan and add the mince, cover with water and bring to the boil. Leave for a minute to simmer and let cool. When it has cooled, the fat will have floated to the top. Skim the fat off the top and then you can add the rest of the ingredients, plus more water, except for the potatoes. Heat up to a boil, simmer for one hour, then add the potatoes and leave simmering for a further twenty-five minutes. Make sure there is enough water left, especially if you have had it boiling fast. Remember, the water that you have let boil away was holding the taste and adding more water halfway through the cooking will just result in a fairly tasteless meal. You will have to practise with the amount of water needed. Some people like lots of thin gravy and others not so much gravy but thicker, so it's really a trial-and-error situation.

Quick cheese sandwich

If you want to cheat on protein and starch, a toasted cheese and tomato sandwich makes a good little filler. A little bit of know-how can be the difference between just cheese on toast and a tasty, light dish. First, toast the bread on one side and then place the grated cheese on the uncooked side of the toast, cook the cheese until it bubbles slightly, add sea salt and pepper to taste, pop on the grill, add the sliced tomatoes, heat until the cheese has melted and serve immediately.

Fish

Smoked mackerel is a very filling, inexpensive light meal, easily bought fresh or in packets (but not in oil in tins) at any of the supermarkets. Serve with either cucumber and tomatoes, new potatoes, or fresh green vegetables.

Grill a fillet of plaice, add a slice of lemon to squeeze on the fish and serve with a baked potato. Scoop out the potato from its skin, mash with yoghurt and put filling back into the potato skin, sprinkle with some parsley or cress. Plaice is very easy to digest and when it's filleted you don't have to struggle with tiny bones.

Eggs

Omelette (they say if you can make a good omelette you can feed a king!)

Chop up a small amount of peppers, a few green pimentos (not hot), a small amount of the green part of the spring onion, salt and pepper to taste (if not restricted for medical problems), 2 or 3 eggs. Lightly beat the eggs with a little milk and pour into a frying pan with a knob of butter or heated sunflower oil (2 teaspoons), let it slightly set, then add the filling. When the underside is still brown but moist, cook for a few minutes and then use a fish slice to lift on to serving plate or dish.

Dessert

Ingredients per serving, 1 large apple, cored, 1 oz of dried fruit mixed with 1 teaspoon of honey which you pile into the centre of the apple. Bake in a moderate oven 200°C / 400°F (Gas Mark 6) for approximately thirty minutes.

Papaya arranged on a plate is very exotic and also has a healing quality.

Yoghurt

There are so many on the market but only a few you should be using.

Ingredients for home-made yoghurt. Heat 1 pint of milk to blood temperature (about 80°F). Mix 2 tbspns of best quality starter yoghurt (such as Losely Farm) into a yoghurt maker or vacuum flask, pour the warm milk over the starter and stir. Close the lid of the yoghurt maker or flask and leave for about eight hours. When making the next batch, use two tablespoons of your own, home-made yoghurt. As long as you always keep two tablespoons of your own product aside, you can always use it as the base to begin again, otherwise you will have to revert to the bought yoghurt.

A BASIC
NUTRITIONAL GUIDE

This is a useful guide when deciding which types of food to include in the diet and which ones to avoid in order to maintain good health. Types of food: *FTB* = foods to avoid and *AF* = acceptable foods.

Beans or pulses – *FTB:* Canned pork and beans, canned beans with salt preservatives; frozen beans. *AF:* All beans cooked without animal fat or salt.

Beverages – *FTB:* Alcohol; coffee; cocoa; pasteurised and sweetened juices; fruit drinks; sodas; tea (except herb tea). *AF:* Herb teas; fresh vegetable and fruit juices; a coffee substitute made from cereal grains instead of coffee beans; mineral water.

Dairy products – *FTB:* All cheeses; all pasteurised cheese products with orange colouring; ice cream. *AF:* Raw goats' (light) cheese; non-fat cottage cheese; Kefir; unsweetened yoghurt; goats' milk; raw or skimmed milk; buttermilk; all soya products.

Eggs – *FTB:* Fried or pickled. *AF:* Boiled or poached (limit to four weekly).

Fish – *FTB:* All fried fish, all shellfish, salted fish, anchovies, herring, fish canned in oil. *AF:* All fresh-water white fish, salmon, broiled or baked fish, water-packed tuna.

Fruits – *FTB:* Canned, bottled, or frozen fruits with sweeteners added. *AF:* All fresh, frozen stewed and dried fruits without sweeteners; unsulphured fruits; home-canned fruits.

Grains and pasta – *FTB:* All white flour products; white rice; spaghetti and macaroni; crackers; overly processed oatmeal and hot or cold cereals. *AF:* All grains and products containing grains; cereals; breads, muffins; whole grain crackers; cream of wheat; rye cereal; buckwheat; millet; oats; brown rice; wild rice (limit yeast breads to three times per week).

Meats – *FTB:* Beef; all forms of pork; hot dogs; luncheon meats; smoked, pickled and processed meats; corned beef; duck; goose; spare ribs; meat gravies; organ meats. *AF:* Skinless turkey, chicken and ham. (Consume meat only three times a week.)

Nuts – *FTB:* Peanuts, all salted or roasted nuts. *AF:* All fresh raw nuts (except peanuts). *Oils (Fats)* – *FTB:* All saturated fats; hydrongenated margarine; refined processed oils; shortenings; hardened oils. *AF:* All cold-pressed oils; corn, sunflower, sesame, olive, soybean, sunflower and canola oils.

Seasonings – *FTB:* Black or white pepper; salt; hot red peppers; white vinegar; all artificial vinegar. *AF:* Garlic; onion; dried parsley; spike; all herbs; chives; cayenne; dried vegetables; apple vinegar; tamari; miso; seaweed, sea salt; dulse.

Soups – *FTB:* Canned with salt or preservatives (MSG), fat stock or creamed. *AF:* Home-made (salt- and fat-free) bean, lentil, pea, vegetable, barley, brown rice, onion.

Sprouts and seeds – *FTB:* Seeds cooked in oil or salt. *AF:* All slightly cooked sprouts (except alfalfa), wheatgrass and all raw seeds.

Sweets – *FTB:* White, brown or raw sugar; corn syrups; chocolate; sugar candy; fructose; all syrups except pure maple syrup; all sugar substitutes; jams and jellies with sugar. *AF:* Barley malt or rice syrup; small amounts of raw honey; pure maple syrup; unsulphured blackstrap molasses.

Vegetables – *FTB:* All canned and frozen with salt or additives. *AF:* All raw, fresh, frozen (no additives) or home-canned. (Cook vegetables only slightly.)

Useful Addresses and Menus

Five top chefs have put together for this book a weight(ish) watchers' diet that does not give the impression that you are slimming. Famous restaurants show you how slimming gourmet food can be, and a top conference caterer gives a sample menu for groups – very useful if you are organising a function.

SEA HORSE

4 THAMESIDE CENTRE, KEW BRIDGE ROAD, BRENTFORD,. MIDDX TW8 0HS

TELEPHONE 0181 568 3040

Smoked Salmon and Sweet Pepper Salad

Quail with Chestnuts, Apples and Calvados served with a selection of seasonal vegetables

Filo Pastry Tartlet filled with Homemade Pear Sorbet and fresh Strawberries

CONCORDIA NOTTE

29–31 CRAVEN ROAD, LONDON W2

TELEPHONE 0171 723 3725 OR 0171 402 4985

Parma Ham and Melon

Spaghetti Napoli

Fresh Strawberries and Ice Cream

Coffee

THE DOME
85 STRAND ON THE GREEN, CHISWICK W4
TELEPHONE 0181 995 6575

French Onion Soup with Cheese Crouton

Field and Oyster Mushrooms with Pine Kernels, sauteed with Garlic, Mixed Leaves and Croutons

Freshly prepared Summer Fruit Salad

EL PRADO
RESTAURANT ESPANOL AND TAPAS BAR
766 FULHAM ROAD, LONDON SW6 5ST
TELEPHONE 0171 731 7179

Mussels in vinaigrette

Grilled breast of Chicken with lightly cooked unsalted vegetables

Plain fruit salad with a slice of lemon

MAMTA
PUR INDIAN VEGETARIAN RESTAURANT
692 FULHAM ROAD, FULHAM, LONDON SW6 5SA
TELEPHONE 0171 736 5914

Steamed rice and black lentil served in lentil and vegetable sambhar

Toful special – fresh vegetable lightly stir-fried with tofu

Bhindi vegetable – lightly spiced fresh ladies fingers cooked in vegetable oil

Puffed lotus savoury – seeds of lotus plant cooked in a savoury tomato sauce containing onion and soya sauce and served on a bed of fresh salad, served with brown rice mushroom and onion

STRINGFELLOWS
16–19 UPPER STREET, MARTINS LANE, LONDON WC2
TELEPHONE 0171 240 5534

*Artichoke heart presented with lightly sauteed mixed wild
mushrooms and asparagus tips*

*Native seabass filo steamed with ginger Indonesian soya
sauce and spring onions, accompanied by pink grapefruit and
blood orange salad*

Lemon souffle with pineapple coulis

Useful Addresses

Dave Prowse (previously a Mr Universe)
The Star Gym, 12 Marshalsea Road, London SE1 1HL
Telephone 0171 407 5650
For fitness and exercise routines

The Blue Stone Clinic
20 Harmont House, 20 Harley Street, London W1N 1AL
Telephone 0171 637 4533
For advice on dietary matters and PEME osteapathy treatment

Valerie Austin
Consultant Hypnotherapist
Telephone 0171 637 1320   FAX 0171 580 8838
For treatment of weight reduction courses, weight loss, luxury holidays, stopping smoking, stress, traumas and phobias etc.

Concordia Restaurant
29 / 31 Craven road, London W2
Telephone 0171 723 3725
An Italian restaurant that discreetly caters for celebrities who need to stay trim

Sea Horse
4 Thameside Centre, Kew Bridge Road,
Brentford, Middlesex TW8 0HS
Telephone 0181 568 3040
A conference and hospitality barge which cruises the Thames

Dr J C Mason DD, DSP
American Centre of Hypnosis
203 Airport N. Office, UMA AT Cook, Fort Wayne,
IN 46825, USA
Telephone (0101 219) 489 3202